"Will you make up your mind, Ben!"

Abby gasped angrily. "First you tell me I'm unfeminine because I don't wear dresses, and when I do...."

"There's a happy medium between looking like an undersized ranch hand and a—" He bit off the rest of his explosive words.

"None of my friends seem to mind that I look like a—whatever you were about to call me," she told him frigidly.

"I'll bet they don't," he muttered and jerked her to him. "I'll show you what every man was thinking about when he stood up to dance with you." Before she had time to close them he had covered her lips with his own. She had wanted Ben to kiss her, but not like this...as if he was punishing her.

Rich + Rose McbEy

OTHER

Harlequin Romances

by ELIZABETH GRAHAM

Many of these titles are available at your local bookseller or through the Harlequin Reader Service.

For a free catalogue listing all available Harlequin Romances, send your name and address to:

HARLEQUIN READER SERVICE,
M.P.O. Box 707, Niagara Falls, N.Y. 14302
Canadian address: Stratford, Ontario, Canada N5A 6W2

or use coupon at back of book.

New Man at Cedar Hills

by

ELIZABETH GRAHAM

Harlequin Books

TORONTO · LONDON · NEW YORK · AMSTERDAM
SYDNEY · HAMBURG · PARIS

PB
FIC
Graham

Original hardcover edition published in 1978
by Mills & Boon Limited

ISBN 0-373-02223-9

Harlequin edition published December 1978

83-11149

CHAPTER ONE

THE man's narrowly directed eyes took in the sign reading
'*Cedar Hills Ranch—A. Mackenzie*' and capable bronzed
hands swung the dust-laden green station wagon off the
hard-topped road and into a tree-lined driveway. A dirt
driveway, bordered on each side by neatly painted white
wood fences enclosing pastures that were as yet brilliant
green, providing succulent cropping for the dozen or so
mares and their foals grazing there.

Light green eyes reached along the length of drive to a
low-set house nestled at its end, appraising the sizeable
structure with a surprised lift of well-marked brows as the
car approached almost silently on the packed earth. Blend-
ing into its surroundings as if it had belonged there for a
long time, the varnished log house had an air of welcome in
its small-paned windows and iron-studded front door, a
welcome less apparent in the clinical neatness of a gravelled
forecourt where the man parked his car.

His leather-booted feet crunched harshly on the gravel
chips as he walked towards the entrance, lean hips taut in
light blue denim, shoulders broad and muscled in matching
jacket.

A plump grey-haired woman, her manner flustered as
if she had been disturbed in an important task, answered
his knock on the thick wooden door, barely glancing at
him as he lifted the broad Stetson from his head and asked
politely:

'Miss Abigail Mackenzie?'

'Oh, you'll be the new man,' the woman said worriedly.
'You'll find Miss Mackenzie in the office just down there.'
She pointed to the far end of the house, and in another

5

moment had disappeared again, closing the door firmly behind her.

The man hesitated, brows drawn down thoughtfully, then his feet took him quietly along the concrete path in the direction indicated. His steps slowed as he approached the attached yet separate addition to the house, hearing voices raised in what was obviously an argument.

'I don't care about that, Dave,' a woman's voice, sounding young, floated out, anger sharpening what would normally be pleasant tones. 'I want those cows moved out next week whether your trucking friends are ready to take them or not! If they can't do it, we'll find somebody else who will!'

'Oh, come on, Abby,' a deep-throated male voice answered roughly, barely concealed impatience tempering the words. 'Another week isn't going to make that much difference, and we get good terms from Jack——'

'*You* get good terms from Jack!'

'What do you mean by that?'

'You know what I mean. Anyway,' a weary note crept into her voice, 'I don't want any loose ends hanging round anywhere. One of the Wests is likely to turn up any day, and there's no way I'm going to let him point a finger at anything here and say I can't run the place myself!'

'Abby!' There was a sound of heavy feet moving over a tiled floor, then the man's voice saying persuasively: 'Why don't you marry me, and then you won't have to worry about the Wests any more? They'd leave you alone if you had a man to run things for you.'

'I don't need a man!' she told him hotly, and Dave laughed softly.

'If I ever saw anybody who needed a man, it's you,' he said thickly.

'Don't touch me, Dave! I don't need you or any other man to help me run this place.'

'Running the place wasn't what I had in mind. It might surprise you to know, Miss Abigail, that there are more things in life than a cattle ranch—very pleasurable things that I should maybe teach you a thing or two about.'

Her cry was muffled suddenly, and the stranger stepped

to the doorway, his eyes taking in at a glance the slim figure of a girl struggling silently with a well-set man whose mouth was clamped to hers, his hands running familiarly over the light blue plaid of her shirt.

'Am I interrupting something?' he asked blandly.

Abby felt herself released suddenly as Dave turned with an oath to the stranger in the doorway. The unknown man removed his hat with lazy grace, revealing hair that was thick and seemed not to know whether to be dark brown or red. There was nothing indeterminate, however, in the hard thrust of chin and firm-lipped mouth under light green eyes.

'Who the hell are you?' Dave whipped out angrily, and the stranger shrugged casually.

'I'm——'

'You must be the new man,' Abby gasped, relief more than a little evident in her smoothing of red-gold hair and tucking in of the shirt that had become loosened from Dave's amorous exploration.

'Wait outside!' Dave snarled.

'No!' Looking again at the stranger's steady-eyed gaze, Abby said: 'Do—do you have experience as a foreman?'

Brown brows lifted slightly in surprise. 'Some,' he admitted. 'But——'

'Good!' said Abby crisply. 'You're hired—and you're fired,' she turned to address Dave with quivering nostrils.

'*What?*' Dave took a belligerent step towards her and blustered menacingly: 'You can't fire me. Your father——'

'My father's dead,' Abby reminded him, her eyes dark blue icicles. 'Whatever plans he had for you and me never had my approval.'

'Why, you——'

Dave took another step towards her, his fair-skinned face flooded with red, but the stranger made a noisy move with his feet at the same time and Dave looked round at him. For long moments their eyes held, metallic green and light blue, then Dave picked up his hat with a savage gesture from the desk.

'You haven't heard the last of me, Abby,' he warned darkly. 'You'll be sorry you did this—you don't even know this guy's name, for Pete's sake!'

'What's your name?' Abby directed at the stranger.

'Ben,' he said slowly. 'Ben Franklin.'

'Well, Ben, meet Dave Corben whose place you're taking.' Abby turned frosty eyes on Dave's livid face. 'I'd appreciate your moving out as soon as possible so that your replacement can get settled in.'

His eyes flashed into the deeper blue of hers for a long moment, then he threw himself out of the office, brushing past the stranger as if he didn't exist.

As soon as he had gone, Abby sank into the chair behind the broad desk and let her shoulders droop, almost forgetting the new man until he asked quietly:

'Do you always act so impulsively? He's right, you know —you don't know anything about me.'

She looked at him without moving the hand covering her forehead under the soft cloud of red-gold hair. Something about the jut of his jaw, the steadiness in his light-coloured eyes, told her that he would be uncompromisingly straight in his dealings with her.

'You'll be on a trial period, Mr—Franklin?' she ended on a note of disbelief. 'Ben—*Franklin*?'

The ghost of a smile touched the outer reaches of his green eyes. 'My mother was a devoted American, and greatly admired Benjamin Franklin.'

'Oh. You say "was"—is your mother dead?'

'A few years ago.'

'And the rest of your family?'

'I haven't seen much of them lately.'

Sensing his unwillingness to talk about his background, and feeling too upset by the recent scene with Dave to insist on more details, Abby launched into a brief description of his duties and the salary he would receive.

'That seems—generous,' he said cautiously. 'Does a spread this size run to that kind of pay for employees?'

Abby shrugged. 'It's what my father gave Dave Corben, and I can't see why you shouldn't get the same if you're worth it.'

His eyes rested for a moment on the full curve of her lips, and she felt an unaccountable flush creep uncomfortably over her honey-toned cheeks. There was something disturbing about the intentness of those green eyes, the confident set of his broad shoulders, that set off a warning bell deep in her subconscious—what the bell warned her against she couldn't at that moment tell.

'You—um—say you have experience. Where, exactly?'

He shrugged and sauntered across to take the chair at the other side of the desk. 'Lately in Texas. I ran a spread quite a bit larger than you have here.'

'You know the size of this ranch?' she frowned, then her brow cleared. 'Oh, I guess Phil Hansen told you when you saw him about the job.' A relieved smile curved the generous outline of her mouth. 'I'm glad you decided to take this job rather than the one you were offered further north. Especially now that Dave——' She frowned again, her slim fingers toying with a pen on the green blotter on the desk. 'It's very important to me, Mr Franklin,' she said in a precise voice, 'that things run smoothly at Cedar Hills. My father died recently, and I—I want to make a success of running the place on my own.' The soft fullness of her lips tightened unconsciously. 'There are people who think I'm incapable of doing that, and I mean to prove them wrong.'

'What people would they be?' he asked cautiously, as if not sure of how interested he was supposed to be in his new employer's affairs.

'Oh, just a few deep-eyed Albertan males who think a female can't do anything without a strong, silent man beside her,' she returned almost absently, the thinking part of her mind embroiled in remembrance of her father's will which had given John West, his old friend from early pioneering days, almost unlimited licence over the running of Cedar Hills Ranch. True, the Albertan head of a huge cattle empire in the next Province had a substantial financial investment in Cedar Hills, but Abby had regarded as a threat his offer to send a member of his family to 'assist' her in the running of the ranch. She suspected that, like her own father, John West and his family were steeped in Old Country traditions that died hard.

Traditions which said that a woman's place was in the home, cooking and baking and supporting the more important work of the men on a ranch. But Abby took a perverse kind of pride in not having cooked more than boiled, or—at a pinch—scrambled eggs in her life, concentrating her energies on the outdoor tasks which were vastly more interesting to her. Her eyes abruptly lost their absent look when she realised that Ben Franklin had asked her a question at least once.

'I'm sorry—what did you say?'

An amused gleam reflected off his green eyes. 'I just asked if you didn't consider a man necessary for—certain things,' he repeated in a voice she was beginning to recognise as holding underlying force in spite of its pleasant masculine tone. 'Children, for instance. Won't you need a man for that? Or don't you mean to carry on the Mackenzie line?'

'They'd hardly be Mackenzies, would they?' she retorted tartly, flushing in a manner she was unaware was attractive in the added colour it lent to her eyes, pointing up their blueness as the sky intensified the depth of lake water. 'One day I'll think about marriage and children,' she added with a faintly defiant air, 'when I've——'

'Proved to these Albertans that you can fill a man's shoes better than he can?' he finished enigmatically when she paused.

'Maybe.' Her head lifted in a listening attitude at the sound of a pick-up truck from not far away. Throwing down the pen she had been playing with, she stood up straight and slim in shirt and close-fitting jeans. 'If you'd like to get your things, Mr Franklin, I think you can move right into your quarters.'

'The name's Ben,' he reminded her, following her trim-hipped figure to the door. Turning to look back at him, Abby found her eyes having to rise far beyond her five foot five stature to the height of his innocuous gaze. Though not as sturdily built as Dave, she knew that in a battle for strength, the stranger would win hands down with his flat-muscled body and determinedly steely chin. Spare, that was what he was, but spare in the strong way that made other men seem as midgets, whatever their size.

'Abby,' she introduced herself briefly, and watched with shadowed eyes as Dave's truck disappeared along the drive, even the ramming shift of gears making clear his angry acceptance of her dismissal. An unconscious sigh escaped her lips. 'If you want to bring your things round the corner, I'll show you where you'll be staying.'

She was standing in front of the neatly contoured log bungalow, a replica in miniature of the main house, when he came from his car bearing only an expertly tooled saddle of light-coloured leather. That, together with the Texas licence plates on his station wagon, piqued Abby's curiosity about his background. The denim clothes he was wearing were similar in type to those worn by many ranch men in the area, but no ordinary cowhand could afford the expensiveness of that saddle.

'Will your wife and family be joining you?' she asked half casually as he followed her into the small bungalow after laying his saddle outside.

'No.' The brief reply told her little more about him, and she made no effort to delve further into his personal life. The rugged rules of their country were unspoken but nonetheless rigid—no one had to volunteer any more information than was strictly necessary.

Evidence of Dave's unexpected departure abounded in the two-bedroomed foreman's house. Rugs covering the polished wood floor in the intimately cosy living room were bunched up as if all Dave's possessions had been dragged across them; dishes were piled in the sink of the small kitchen adjoining it; the bed he had used an unmade mess.

'I—I'll get Harry to come down and fix things up a little,' Abby apologised.

'Harry?'

'Harriet—Mrs James, the housekeeper.'

'Oh, yes. The one who told me where to find you.'

'I guess so, if you went to the house first. She takes care of the housekeeping and her husband, Phil, looks after a million and one things around the ranch, including the gardens.'

'Gardens?' he queried absently, his eyes sharply appraising the accommodation he would be occupying for the immediate future.

'He supplies fresh vegetables in season, and takes care of the flower garden behind the house.' Abby moved up behind the tall stranger as he pulled open the fridge door, seeing its emptiness at the same time as he did. 'Maybe you'd better have dinner at the main house tonight. Harry will be going into town for supplies tomorrow, so you can tell her what you want then.'

'I cook for myself normally?' he asked, turning the full battery of the green eyes on her uplifted face.

Abby shrugged. 'Unless you want to eat with the un-married men in the bunkhouse. Dave always preferred to fix his own, unless . . .'

'Unless you came and cooked it for him?' he supplied, tongue in cheek.

'No!' A scornful laugh rose from Abby's throat. 'I'm not the domesticated type, Mr—*Ben*,' she told him, her hand nevertheless going up unconsciously to straighten the red checked gingham curtain at the small window. 'You'll find there are quite a few unattached females in the district who'll be more than happy to fulfil any—needs you might have.'

'Good,' he said, unperturbed, as he followed her back into the living room, where evidence of previous fires still remained in the rock-faced fireplace along the far wall. 'But I think I can take care of most of my—needs—myself.'

For no reason that she could think of, this brought a flood of colour to Abby's cheeks and she went with small booted feet to the door, hardly turning to say:

'I'll expect you at seven, then. I can give you a rundown on your duties while we eat.'

'What better aid to digestion could there be?' he asked gravely as they emerged again into the late afternoon sun. Abby looked sharply back at him, but detected no slant of humour on his leanly handsome face. She continued on into the house while he crossed again to his car, presumably to get the rest of his things. Mentally shrugging, Abby decided that she could find out more about the stranger over the meal they would share later.

'Harry?' Her feet alternately clicked over the polished wood of the spacious hall and became muffled on the thick animal fur rugs scattered across it. At the entrance to the farm-sized kitchen she paused, her hands on either side of the doorframe as she leaned inward to the deliciously warm and aromatic kitchen. Harry looked up from the oven door she was closing, her plump face reddened from the heat.

'There'll be another one for dinner,' Abby told her, sniffing appreciatively. 'What are we having?'

'Braised rib steaks—I can put another potato in to bake. Is it the new man?'

'Mmm.' The girl came further into the room and picked up a piece of celery from the cleaned ingredients for salad, her small white teeth crunching healthily on it. 'I'm starved!'

'Well, don't eat like a field hand in front of the new man,' Harry said caustically, her light brown eyes going over the girl's whipcord-lean figure. 'Are you going to change into a dress?'

Abby's eyes widened. 'Why would I do that? He's just a man like any other ...'

'One day, Abby Mackenzie, you're going to wake up to the fact that all men aren't alike, and some like women to look like women.' The housekeeper's gaze sharpened. 'Why is he coming here to eat, anyway? I'd have thought the bunkhouse was the place for one of the men.'

'Oh yes, I haven't told you. He's not just one of the hands—I fired Dave and made this Ben Franklin the foreman.'

Harry's mouth dropped open in a horrified gasp. 'You *what*?'

'I fired Dave,' Abby returned with more calmness than she was feeling. 'He got fresh with me, and I didn't like it, so I fired him.'

'You ... But I thought your dad——'

'Dad wasn't the one who had Dave's big hands pawing all over him!' Abby snapped, twirling away to the door. 'If that's what love and marriage is all about, then I'll gladly stay single!'

The housekeeper shook her head as the girl marched away from the kitchen, sighing as she turned back to her chores. Abby, ruffled, stripped off the clothes she was wearing and stepped under a cleansing hot shower, glad to rid her skin of the feel of Dave's man's hands that had scorched through the light cotton of her shirt to the firmly soft flesh below. Even the memory of his lustful seeking sent shudders through her—the aggressive passion rᶜ an older man of Dave's type was far removed from the light lovemaking she had indulged in with boys she had grown up and gone to school with.

Padding back to her bedroom, which had the spartan, clear-cut look she liked in preference to the frilled impedimenta her friends surrounded themselves with, she changed into an outfit not unlike the one she had worn all day. This time, the shirt was of a solid deeper blue that brought her eyes to the colour of summer skies, and slacks of navy polyester which clung to the shape of her softly contoured hips and slenderly formed legs. Dropping to the dressing table stool, she picked up a stiff hairbrush and began to stroke vigorously the shining red-gold hair ... not with any thought of beautifying herself particularly, but because the rhythmic motion was soothing to her disturbed state of mind.

Few people, except perhaps Harriet who had acted as a mother to her from the time of her mother's death when she was five, knew of the turmoil that shook Abby from time to time. Inarticulate longings, more frequent since her father's death six months before, unsteadied her balance in a man-ruled world surrounding her, just when she needed to prove herself an equal in that world. While her father lived, she had felt her worth as a valued helper and companion, needing no more than his words of praise now and then to keep her content. Though he was not a man given to showing affection, there was nevertheless a close bond between them, so that his death had been a blow to her in more ways than one.

Sometimes she felt like a cub abandoned by its parents, alone in facing a world that could be cruel if one was helpless. But that was something she had determined never to be. Helplessness spoke of weakness, and no child of her proudly arrogant father could ever admit to weakness. Early in her life, Adam Mackenzie had instilled into his daughter a spirit of independence, and a legacy of ungiving determination from her Scottish forebears. No one—man or woman—could take away that fierce pride of being her own person. Least of all Dave Corben.

The taut stringing of her nerves tonight was simply a feminine reaction to dismissing him, to knowing that his bulky presence would no longer come between her and the ranch employees he controlled. But she would survive—with or without the help of the new man, whose qualities she had not yet tested.

Whatever she had been prepared for, it was not the smoothly handsome man in dark grey suit and lighter grey silky shirt who presented himself at the door promptly at seven. Nor had she anticipated that his light-coloured eyes would go over her casual garb with a faintly censorious air that spoke volumes.

Feeling inordinately nettled, as being at a disadvantage always did, Abby led him into the low-ceilinged living room with its air of relaxed country comfort and brought him the whisky and soda he had asked for, at the same time carrying her own glass of light sherry to sit opposite him in one of the chintz-covered armchairs edging the fireplace.

'Well, Mr Franklin,' she said, her voice purposely brittle, 'this seems as good a time as any to tell me something about yourself.'

'What exactly do you want to know—Abby?' he stressed, seeming gratified by the pink sweep of colour to her honey-toned cheeks.

'Well, you can start by telling me what you were doing in Texas. You're not an American, are you?'

'No. At least, only half so.'

'Oh yes, your patriotic mother,' she smiled tightly. 'Are there any more like you at home?'

His eyes regarded her cautiously. 'I have—three brothers, if that's what you mean.'

'Really? Don't tell me there's a George Washington and an Abraham Lincoln too!'

'George is my oldest brother,' he returned gravely. 'Linc is the youngest—my mother drew the line at naming one of her sons Abraham.'

In a sudden release of pressure, mirth bubbled from

Abby's throat and filled the dark violet of her eyes. 'So let's see, what have we? George Washington, Benjamin Franklin, Lincoln—didn't you say there was another brother?'

'John Adams. Mother was hoping to go on to Andrew Jackson and Daniel Boone, but the line finished after Linc.'

'It must have been nice to be brought up in a big family like yours,' she said with unconscious wistfulness.

'It has its drawbacks,' he consoled her drily. 'Boys spend a lot of their time fighting—and Dad would have welcomed a daughter he could spoil. Now he has to make do with . . .'

'Daughters-in-law?' she supplied when he paused, her mind still entranced with the idea of belonging to a big family, quarrels or not.

'That's about it.'

'Your brothers are married?'

'Linc isn't—he's just twenty-two. George and——'

Harry said from the door: 'Supper's ready when you are, Abby.'

'We'll go right in,' said Abby, rising. 'You haven't met our new foreman, have you, Harry?'

'We did meet for a minute,' Ben put in, seeming to dominate the room when he rose too.

The housekeeper's eyes went over his tautly knit body and came back to his level-eyed look. 'Yes, we did,' she said, as if reserving judgment as to his desirability as a foreman at Cedar Hills. 'I'll bring in the soup then.'

'Is she your watchdog?' Ben asked as he followed Abby into the dining room across the hall. It was a room that cried out for a chance to entertain a lot more people than the two who seated themselves at one end of the long table.

'Watchdog? Why should I need one?'

The pale green of his eyes went lazily over her figure as she sat down at the head of the table. 'I would guess you're desirable in more ways than one,' he remarked pointedly. 'There can't be many girls who have your—physical attributes, and a ranch to boot.'

Abby coloured, but was saved from replying by the arrival of Harry with the thick-bodied soup which the new manager attacked with gusto, making her wonder how long

it had been since he had eaten a proper meal. Her own
appetite was unabated, and there was a mutually agreeable
silence between them as they drained the bowls and received the succulent ribs of beef topped with rich gravy
which Harry brought in with scarcely a pause between one
course and the other.

'Whew! That was terrific,' Ben said when the housekeeper came in to remove their plates. 'I haven't eaten food
like that since my mother——' He broke off, but Harry
beamed anyway as she lifted his cleaned plate from in
front of him.

'If you always ate that heartily, you must have been a joy
to your mother,' she said comfortably. 'Now, would you
like blueberry pie, or just coffee?'

Abby, piqued that the housekeeper's words had been
addressed exclusively to the new man, said sharply:
'Coffee, please, Harry,' a frown settling on her brow when
Ben responded enthusiastically:

'I can't turn down blueberry pie! That has to be my
favourite dessert.'

'You'll have it in just a minute,' Harry assured him and,
her plump face wreathed in smiles, hurried out to comply
with his order.

'Well, if you can please me with your ranch skills as much
as you've delighted Harry with your appreciation of her
cooking, you might be staying around Cedar Hills for some
time!' Abby remarked tartly, her fingers playing agitatedly
with her dessert fork.

'I don't think you'll have any cause for complaints,' he
returned evenly, eyeing her flushed face appraisingly.

'Good. You still haven't told me what you were doing in
Texas.'

'I worked on a big spread there, doing something of
everything.'

'You had no particular job to do?'

'The owner was ill—I filled in for him where I could.'

'Oh. So you have all-round experience?'

Harry's ample figure bustled in at that point, pride evident in the flourish with which she placed the deep-browned
blueberry pie in front of Ben.

'Thanks, Harry, that looks out of this world,' he drawled appreciatively, and Abby looked sharply at the pleased housekeeper.

'I'll have my coffee too, Harry,' she reminded her.

'Coming right up, Abby,' and, true to her word, Harry brought in a pot of coffee and the necessary accoutrements on a tray, placing it beside Abby.

'Yes,' Ben answered as if there had been no interruption. 'I have a fair amount of experience. I was brought up on a ranch.'

The light flick of his eyes brought an unaccountable flush to her cheeks, then his head was bent over the crumbly pastry with its filling of purple berries. For a moment, Abby had a chance to inspect the reddish-brown hair, brushed neatly back over his crown in honour of the occasion, the uncompromising tilt of his jaw, the proud straightness of nose above lips that were full and well-shaped but firmly held as if their owner would stand no nonsense from any quarter. The hand wielding the dessert fork was long-fingered with blunt businesslike nails cut short in keeping with the masculine show of short brown hairs on its back and on the part of his wrist showing under the light grey cuff of his shirt.

A man's man, she thought involuntarily—surely one who could control the more boisterous elements of the Cedar Hills' employees? The brawny, muscular ones who resented taking orders from a woman.

'Do you mind if I smoke while we have coffee?' Ben interrupted her thoughts, looking pointedly at the untouched pot.

'No . . . no, go ahead. There's an ashtray further down the table.' Abby's hands went quickly into action then, pouring coffee into their cups while Ben reached into his breast pocket to extract a thin-line cigar and matches.

'What do you take in your coffee?'

'Sugar—two spoons. No cream.'

Was he always so precise about his requirements? Abby wondered as she passed his cup to him. For no reason that she could think of, his avowal that he could take care of most of his needs himself came vividly to mind. Most, he had said. Scornfully, she knew she had to look no further than the sensuous curve of his lips to know which one he couldn't take care of himself. A woman—and she surmised he would not have to look far to find one—was necessary to fill that particular need.

'Will your wife be joining you later on?' she asked conversationally, but his mouth quirked down at the corners in amusement as if he knew exactly what her thought processes had been.

'No. Is that important for the job?'

'Of course not. I—just wondered, that's all. It's a big bungalow for a man on his own.'

'No bigger than it was for your previous foreman,' he pointed out reasonably.

'I suppose not.' Suddenly wanting to change the subject, she looked frankly into the light green of his eyes. 'It's—very important to me that the ranch should be run efficiently and profitably.'

'So you said. You have something to prove to—who was it?'

A frown descended between the dark gold of her brows. 'The Wests. They have a big spread in Alberta—Cedar Hills would just be a drop in the bucket to them, but ...' she bit her lip and looked down into the brown coffee in her cup, '... well, it's a long story.'

'I have lots of time,' Ben said quietly, narrowing his eyes against the cigar smoke curling round his face.

'Well,' she sighed, 'Dad knew John West years ago when they both homesteaded in British Columbia. Things weren't going too well, so John West moved to Alberta where he picked up title to a good-sized property for next to nothing. Luck seemed to dog his footsteps almost more than bad fortune tracked my father ... John made out well on his first property, and over the years he acquired more and more land until today I believe he has one of the biggest places going.' Her lashes swept down over her cheeks, casting a shadow on the fineness of her clear skin.

'Dad went from bad to worse until, after my mother died, he was at rock bottom. John West stepped in and put up the money for this place if Dad would run it. Dad hated to accept what amounted to charity, I guess, but he had me by then so he hadn't much choice. And over the years since then, he's paid back more than half of John West's outlay.' There was an almost desperate plea for understanding in the blue eyes she trained on Ben's. 'It was very important to Dad that he should prove himself as good a rancher as the man he had shared hardships with early on.'

'That's understandable,' Ben said gruffly. 'A man has to prove his worth.'

'Yes, that's it exactly.' Abby looked pleased at his understanding. 'It was important to Dad, and now it's important to me ... but there's something else I have to contend with that didn't affect Dad.' Bitterness compressed the soft line of her mouth. 'The Wests—John and both of his sons —seem to think a woman incapable of safeguarding their investment at Cedar Hills.'

Ben cleared his throat. 'Maybe they think you're a little young for such a responsibility?' he suggested quietly, a smile partially obscured by the narrowing of his lids when she flared:

'I'm almost twenty-two! But if I was fifty-two, those Wests would still think I'm a helpless, incapable female who can't function without a man.'

'You've met them?'

'No, and I don't want to! I don't have to see them to know that they're arrogant, self-seeking empire-builders who treat their wives as chattels who do their master's bidding in the kitchen and be——' She broke off abruptly, horrified that the thoughts she had kept exclusively hers had been spilled out to this veritable stranger.

'Bedroom?' he finished softly, an amused smile in his voice. 'Don't you think a wife's place is in the kitchen and —bedroom?'

His meaningful pause sent colour cascading into Abby's face, her fingers trembling as she picked up the coffee pot and dumped fresh liquid into his cup and hers.

'No, I don't!' she said violently. 'And I'll never understand the women who pretend they're satisfied with cooking and dusting and—the rest of it. I'll always want to be where the real action's going on.'

The green eyes regarded her quizzically. 'Didn't it ever occur to you that those other women might consider their own sphere of operations is where the real action is?'

Nonplussed, she stared belligerently back at him. 'If it had, I'd have discounted it right away. No woman in her right mind would be content to stagnate in a man's shadow!'

'Lucky for men that all women don't feel the same way,' he commented drily, rising without giving the impression of being incensed at her forcibly expressed opinions, yet having an assurance far beyond that of most newly hired ranch foremen.

'You're leaving already?' Abby rose to her feet too, conscious of his height in a way Dave's had never made her aware of. Shocked remembrance made her hand fly to her mouth. 'Oh! I completely forgot to ask Harry to——'

'It's okay, I've made the place reasonably habitable for tonight. But I'd appreciate a woman's touch on it tomorrow.' The ghost of a smile flickered in his eyes for a moment, then disappeared. 'I'd like to make a long-distance phone call, if you've no objection. A collect call,' he stressed, letting her know that he didn't expect the Cedar Hills account to pay for it.

'Yes ... yes, there's a phone in the hall right over there.'

'Is that the only one? It's a private call.'

'No,' she said slowly. 'There's one in the office.'

'May I use that one?'

'Certainly,' she replied coolly. 'I'll let you have the key and you can return it in the morning.'

'Thanks. And thanks for a great dinner,' he turned back to say in the hall, a smile deepening the lines radiating from his eyes. He must be about thirty, Abby thought irrelevantly, and he was very attractive ... if a girl liked the rugged he-man look. She handed him the key and saw him out of the front door, leaning with her back to it after he had gone, her brow knitted thoughtfully. An attractive, yet a mysterious man who had seemed to divulge a lot about himself yet told her very little. About whether he was married, for instance. Somehow, from his defence of woman's place being in the home, she imagined he must be. Moving off, she paused in front of the telephone extension, staring hard at it before taking another few steps. Never in her life had she eavesdropped on a private phone call, yet didn't she owe it to herself and the ranch to know as much as possible about this stranger whom she had impulsively promoted to foreman from the job he had originally expected to be offered?

Quietly, and holding her breath in case even that revealed her presence on the line, she lifted the extension and put it to her ear. Ben Franklin must have dialled the number because the ringing tone sounded several times before it ceased abruptly in mid-tone and a huskily breathless woman's voice said: 'Hello?'

'Sylvia?'

'Ben?' Evidently delighted, the woman continued: 'Ben darling, where are you? We've been expecting you home . . .'

Abby replaced the receiver stealthily, an unfamiliar sickness welling up inside her. 'We've been expecting you home' —it was obvious that the new foreman not only had a wife, but at least one child as well.

One question nagged at her even as she lay in her bed, moonlight shafting across the white bedspread. The woman —his wife—had obviously expected that Ben would have returned to his home. Why then had he accepted the job of foreman at Cedar Hills Ranch?

CHAPTER TWO

ABBY watched the last of the cattle trucks lumber out and away from the ranch and turned with a satisfied smile to Ben, who came to join her at the white-painted rail fence opposite the house. He was dressed in fawn denim, and his face bore the dusty streaks that spoke of hard work, and lots of it, loading Cedar Hills cattle on to the trucks which would bear them to the railroad cars for onward shipment to far-flung markets.

'I almost wish old John West hadn't written to say that none of his family could spare the time to come to Cedar Hills right now,' she crowed exultantly. 'I won't even see his face when he receives the quarterly payment on the loan!' She shook her head regretfully, but the sparkle remained in her eyes.

'That's important to you?'

'You bet it is! I'm out to prove something to the Wests, and this is the best way I know how.' She turned impulsively to him. 'Let's go into the house and celebrate.'

'Not right now, Abby. I have a few things to see to before calling it a day.' There was an almost imperceptible shift of his eyes to where Walt Penman, the biggest and most aggressive of the ranch hands, walked with his deliberate gait from the pasture behind them. His small set eyes darted inquisitive looks in their direction as he passed not far from them, and Abby felt the shudder down her spine which Walt's appearance always gave her. An old friend of Dave Corben's, who had hired him some months before her father's death, Walt had small eyes that always seemed to Abby to hold an animal-like leer whenever she came in contact with him. Which was as seldom as possible, she told herself thankfully, watching Ben's easy pace as he walked towards the other man.

Had Ben refused her invitation to the house for a drink because of Walt's presence? Though why that should be, she couldn't think. In the eight days since his arrival, Ben had taken over the smooth running of the ranch with little noticeable effort, the men, with one or two exceptions like Walt, appearing to accept his quiet air of authority without demur. Several times in the past week, Abby had noted the respect they accorded him when he demonstrated his ability in yet another area demanding skill and coolheadedness. Already she could pick out his lean figure from a distance, even in a milling throng of men and horses and cows. Whatever else might be mysterious in his background, the fact that he had been born to a saddle was not.

Now as she walked towards the house, Abby's brow wrinkled in thought. She knew no more about him than she had at the beginning—except that he had a wife named Sylvia ... a woman who called him 'Ben darling.' Obviously she wouldn't call him 'darling' if there had been a quarrel between them, but if they were on good terms why wasn't he with her wherever she lived, or planning on bringing her to Cedar Hills? Abby sighed in annoyance, but whether at her own piqued interest in the handsome stranger or at his reticence she wasn't sure.

Harry was busy ironing in the kitchen when she wandered in there, the thought of a celebration drink faded from her mind—there was no fun or triumph in a solitary celebration —and pulled up short when she saw the stack of lovingly ironed shirts in various shades of cotton and denim. Harry's husband, Phil, she knew, wore mostly dark green work clothes bought from the Sears catalogue at regular intervals.

'Whose laundry are you doing?' she demanded.

Harry looked up half apologetically, half defiantly. 'The new man's. He——'

'Well, of all the nerve! How dare he ask you to do his laundry for him!'

'He didn't ask me, I offered,' Harry returned, complacency restored as she concentrated again on the grey shirt Ben had worn to the house for dinner on his first night.

'He's a man used to being taken care of, Abby, I can tell. If he was one of my boys, I'd be grateful if——'

'Oh, he's used to being taken care of, all right!' Abby snapped. 'But if he doesn't care to bring——' Just in time, she stemmed the impulsively angry words and bit her lip, though the sparkle remained in her darkened blue eyes.

'Bring what?' Harry questioned, unperturbed. 'His wife?'

Abby's head lifted and she fixed the housekeeper with curious eyes. 'He told you he has a wife?'

'Not in so many words. But it stands to reason a man like that wouldn't be left hanging on the tree for any length of time.' Harry chuckled and placed the grey shirt carefully on top of the pile. 'He must have had girls coming out of his ears even as a teenager—I can remember what it was like with Jimmy, my oldest boy. And, come to think of it,' thoughtfully, 'this Ben Franklin reminds me a little of Jimmy.'

'Well, he's not Jimmy,' Abby snapped, turning away. 'And I'd appreciate it if you'd stop doing his washing in my house. He has an iron supplied in the bungalow.'

Harry's mouth tightened in a way Abby well remembered from childhood. 'Then I'll go down there and use that one —on my own time!' she added pointedly, and Abby whipped back to stare at her disbelievingly.

'You're not serious?'

'Certainly I am. I like the man, and not even you can tell me who my friends will be.'

Giving an exasperated sigh, Abby stormed out of the kitchen, leaving Harry shaking her head despairingly at her trim hips which somehow conveyed her scorn at the housekeeper's easy capitulation to the new man's good looks.

In the office, Abby slammed a sizeable record ledger on to the desk and threw herself into the swivel chair behind it, but her eyes refused to take in the hastily scrawled entries at the page she opened the green-covered book to. How could Harry have subjected herself to the extra work of doing Ben Franklin's laundry just because he had flattered her over her cooking the night of his arrival? Motherly she might be, but Harry was no fool—yet this man had wormed his way into her good graces until she was willing to stand on ageing legs longer hours than necessary for his sake.

Realisation that the receipts she needed for the entries were still in Ben's possession brought Abby to her feet with an annoyed exclamation. She glanced at the man-sized watch strapped to her wrist as her heels tapped impatiently across the tiled floor to the door. The foreman might still be around the corrals somewhere, and she would make it clear that in future ranch receipts were her responsibility, not his.

Her clear blue eyes scanned the more distant working areas of the ranch, then turned to the small foreman's house, it's partly open door informing her of Ben's presence there. Good. No one else would be around while she told Mr Benjamin Franklin that his area of operations was bounded by the corrals and barns on the practical side.

A peremptory knock on the door produced nothing but a widening of its rough surface, and Abby was about to turn away when her eye was caught by the neatly ironed pile of laundry on the table near the kitchen. Harry must have promised him speedy delivery service, she thought, a flame of anger igniting her steps to take her into the small living room. From the shirts, her gaze went round the transformed appearance of the room from its newly washed curtains to the freshly laid fire in the cleaned grate. More of Harry's work, she fumed.

'Is this your day for inspecting the hired hands' quarters?' a sarcastic voice came from behind her, and she whirled round, the tight compression of her lips relaxing in a startled gasp when she saw Ben Franklin's semi-nude figure outlined against the dim passage beyond. Obviously he had just come from the shower, his only covering a white towel fastened loosely round his hips, and Abby's shocked eyes went from the tousled dampness of his dark brownish red hair over the sleek wetness of wide brown torso to long muscled legs and bare feet.

'Haven't you ever seen a man's body before?' he mocked, and hot colour swept up under Abby's skin, making her eyes sparkle as they met the sardonic gleam in his.

'Of course I have. It—it just surprised me to see you there, that's all,' she lied.

It was true she had seen some of the ranch hands stripped to the waist for some of the chores around the ranch, and of course the boys who had made up swimming parties at the lakes far more scantily covered than Ben Franklin was now, but there was a difference. For one thing, the small room lent an air of intimacy which casual outdoor encounters lacked—and for another, Ben's tightly packed shoulders and chest, molten bronze from long hours of exposure to hot Texas sunshine, exuded a potent aura of masculinity that brought an unexpected tightness to Abby's throat, a dryness to her lips.

'It surprises you to find me in my own place?' Well-outlined brows were lifted in an arc of assumed astonishment, then dropped as a mocking smile returned to the green eyes. 'Or maybe you've been missing your visits to the previous occupant? Though I'd say it's a little early for affairs of the heart to begin!'

Abby's gasp was quickly followed by the hot words that leapt to her lips. 'Don't flatter yourself, Ben Franklin! You'll find I'm not as gullible as Harry where your charms are concerned!'

'No?' He moved forward insinuatingly, and she took a hasty step backward. 'We'll have to see about that, won't we? It could be quite a challenge getting you to change your mind—or is that your idea?' His voice dropped to a lower, snider key. 'You play the part of a man-hater so that he'll be put on his mettle to prove he's the one who can break you down? Well,' he was standing so close to her now that she could feel the masculine vibrations from his muscular body, 'I never could resist that kind of challenge.'

Her startled cry was cut off as he reached out suddenly and pulled her to him, his mouth fastened deliberately over the parted softness of hers and moving there with forceful intent so that her mind recoiled. Never had she been kissed before by a man so sure of himself, so sure of the reaction he would elicit. Her brain reeled, and she put up her hands to push frantically against the damp hardness of his chest, but the feel of prickly short hairs on her palms only increased her dizzy spiral into mindlessness and her hands crept upward slowly to clutch the cool smoothness of his shoulders for support.

And then a strange thing happened to her. She seemed to have reached beyond the numbness of shock to a plateau she had never visited before or even dreamed of. A plateau that ended with a steeply rising hill which attracted and repelled her at the same time. Ben's lips, softening as his body hardened against the limp compliance of hers, urged her on to scale those heights with their sensuously slow probing, his hands moulding her body to the demanding shape of his. Response, blazing suddenly in an Abigail Mackenzie she had never even suspected of existing, strained her pliant form upward to meet the growing urgency of his, her mouth returning pressure for pressure until another sound penetrated her consciousness with shattering force.

'Sorry, Ben—*Abby*?'

The shocked tones of Joe, the youngest of the hands, brought Abby and Ben apart far quicker than a douse of cold water could have. Joe, his brown hair unruly as always, his startled jaw dropped open, was staring at them from the open doorway as Abby pulled abruptly away from Ben, shamed colour staining the already warm pink of her cheeks.

'On the table,' Ben said tersely, stepping back when Joe came sheepishly to lift an expensive-looking camera from the table. 'I'll show you later how it works.'

'Th-thanks, Ben ... sorry, I——'

'It's okay, Joe, you didn't interrupt anything important.'

'Oh.' His disbelief in Ben's assurance patent, Joe backed to the door. 'Thanks, Ben ... see you later.'

'I hope you're satisfied,' Abby flared when the boy had stumbled out. 'Now it's going to be all over the ranch that I'm—that you and I were——' She floundered to a stop and he put in with smooth insolence:

'That you and I were making love? I'd have thought that the rumour you're a woman who reacts normally to a man would be far more preferable than the current one that you're frozen from the neck down!'

'How dare they judge me—*talk* about me that way!' she spluttered, unbidden tears thickening her voice.

'You'd be surprised at the topics of conversation a bunch of ranch hands come up with,' he told her drily, picking up a package of thin cigars from behind the shirts and lighting one with steady hands, looking faintly incongruous in the white towel as he stood inhaling deeply. 'But you can rest assured that now they'll have a different attitude towards you.'

Anger sparked again in her. 'It's an attitude I've never sought and don't care for!' she snapped, stepping smartly to the door, tucking in her loosened shirt as she went.

'No?' his voice followed her suggestively. 'I'm willing to bet a year's wages that you'll be in here begging for more before too much time passes. I detected quite a lot of promise in your not-so-unwilling response to the female function!'

'You—you conceited ...' Her voice faded away in her impotent search for a blistering label to put on his male ego. 'You forget, Mr Franklin, that I can fire you just as fast as I did Dave Corben!'

His mouth curved in a mocking smile. 'And for the same reason! Why are you so afraid of admitting what most women know instinctively, Abby Mackenzie? That they find themselves in relation to men? It's as old as time and it'll go on as long as time lasts.'

'That's your male view, naturally,' she threw back scornfully. 'It suits men to have women wait on them hand and foot and pander to their—animal desires.'

'It's been my experience that women have the same animal desires ... if they'll let themselves feel them.' His eyes were narrowed against the smoke rising from the cigar between his teeth, though she detected the sarcastic gleam there nevertheless. 'But you're beginning to shape up very nicely. In time——'

'That's time you don't have, Mr Franklin!' she snapped. 'You can pick up the wages owing to you ...'

His confident shake of the head stilled the words in her mouth. 'No, Abby, you can't fire me. You need me a lot more than I need you right now if you want to press on with your vendetta against the Wests, which seems to be your guiding light in life.' Digressing, he added thoughtfully:

'I wonder if that's why you've neglected the more rewarding aspects of a girl's life? You feel such hate for these people you've never even met that it fills every emotion you're capable of.'

Abby hardly heard the last quietly spoken words, so intent was she on digesting the indisputable fact that he was right in his assumption that she needed him at that moment. In two more weeks, the cattle would be moved further north to summer pastures higher up in the hills and, much as she hated to admit it, Ben Franklin's quiet authority was required for the smooth running of that operation. Whatever her personal opinion of him might be, his control over the sometimes rough employees was indisputable. She could never find another manager in time for the drive north, unless she asked Dave Corben to return, and that she would never do.

As if he had read her thoughts, Ben said: 'You see what I mean, Abby? Leave the man's work to me—a cattle camp is no place for a woman.'

'I always go on the cattle drives,' she responded automatically.

'Maybe so, but that doesn't mean the men appreciate a lone female in the middle of them.'

'They've never complained to me,' her voice came with stringent hardness.

'Would you expect them to tell the boss's daughter that they don't like having to curb their language when she's around, or avoid the subject that most interests them?'

'Women, I suppose!'

'Right.'

'Men!' she said scornfully. 'All they seem to do is think about girls in the most basic way there is!'

'Don't women do the same thing? Haven't you ever discussed the latest boy-friend with a girl you know?'

Abby's mouth opened to deny the charge, closing suddenly when she recalled protracted hours of dreamy conversation over a new boy in the area—but that had been years ago, when she and Debby had been sixteen and highly impressionable.

'Not lately,' she said briefly, and turned to yank open the

door, which Joe had discreetly closed after him.

Ben's knowing smile pursued her all the way to the office, where she paused to collect her wits. Too late she realised that she had not asked him for the receipts for that day's sales, her reason for going in search of him. Nor had she let him know how she felt about her housekeeper becoming a slave to his attractions. They were many, she admitted honestly, but only if a person was susceptible to them —which she herself was not. The response his kiss had elicited from her was nothing more than the aftermath of shock at his sudden assault on her unsuspecting senses. All he had proved was that she had inner resources which had lain dormant through the years of her maturity, resources which would come to fruition with a man far removed from Ben Franklin's type. A man who wasn't steeped in the tradition of woman's place being in the home while he went out to take care of the more elemental aspects of survival. A man who looked on their partnership as a true sharing of tasks, a man who wasn't—*married*!

Abby sat up abruptly in the chair, her hands tightening to white knuckled intensity on the pen she held between her fingers. Ben was married, and yet he had kissed her as if he was completely free to do so! Why hadn't she remembered at the time? It would have been the ultimate answer to his arrogant self-confidence. But even as the thought formed, she knew she could never have used the information without giving away the fact that she had eavesdropped on his conversation with his wife the night of his arrival.

'Damn you, Ben Franklin!' she muttered half aloud. How typical of his kind of man, who thought a woman's sole purpose in life was to satisfy his present needs regardless of other responsibilities in the background. Again she heard the husky: 'Ben darling,' and acrid bile rose in her throat. Her own unwitting response to his experienced lovemaking now brought a feeling of nausea deep in the being he had touched with his fire. How could she have forgotten? Well, she thought grimly as she rose to her feet, I won't forget again. Whether the warning was for him or for herself, she would not have been able to answer right then.

*

'Why won't you let me drive you into town as long as we're both going there?' Ben persisted two days later when the men had drifted back to their varied chores around the buildings after a break for the coffee provided by the bunk-house cook.

'Because it's not necessary that both of us should be absent at the same time,' Abby reiterated stubbornly. 'I can see to anything you need in town.'

'I doubt if the bank manager would care for even the well-known Abby Mackenzie transacting my business!' he riposted drily, rising to his six feet two or three height. 'If you're worried about me taking too much time off from work, I'll remind you that this is the first time I've been to town since I came to Cedar Hills.'

'I know that,' she said in a low voice, rising herself, trim in neatly fitting jeans and blue plaid shirt. 'If you need— well, if you need an advance, I can let you have——'

'No need,' he interrupted brusquely, standing to one side while holding the door open for her. 'There are some things a man has to take care of himself.' They stepped out to the hard packed earth path in front of the long building. Already the sun's early summer warmth had brought a dryness to the light soil, and Abby's eyes went automatically to the cedar-clad slopes of the background hills as if expecting to see the trees from which the ranch took its name licked by the ever-present threat of destructive flames.

'All right,' she relented suddenly in an access of weariness. 'Be ready in half an hour——'

'No. You be ready in twenty minutes, and we'll go in my car,' he stated unequivocally before striding off in the direction of the small calf corral, and Abby stared after him resentfully before turning with a shrug to go and pay a visit to Glory, her own special horse given to her by her father five years before. Visits had become more frequent as Glory approached the time of her confinement, and Abby well knew the welcome she would receive from the chestnut mare with her soft expressive eyes and sleekly groomed flanks.

'Hi, sweetie,' she murmured, pulling the prospective mother's head down to nuzzle her cheek against the velvet muzzle. 'How's Mamma today? You're a lucky lady, do you know that? Soon you'll have your very own baby to take care of . . . you'll show him where to find the best grass, and how he has to stay close to you for protection.' She laughed softly and patted the rise of Glory's elegantly raised neck. 'You'll be the most important being in his world, won't that be something?'

The mare blew happily through her wide nostrils as if she understood every word Abby spoke, her ears pricking up attentively as the girl went on speaking in her familiar tones.

It was a full five minutes later when Abby left the horse's stall close to the stable entrance, and her eyes narrowed when she saw Ben's well-knit figure disappearing into his bungalow. Could he have heard her nonsensical chatter to the horse? What if he had? she shrugged dismissingly. No doubt a horse who fulfilled her natural function was no more important to him than a woman who did the same thing. This reminded her of the scene enacted between them two days before, and her face still contained a polite blankness when Ben drove the dark green station wagon to the front door of the main house ten minutes later.

His eyes ran over her jeans and shirt and he made no attempt to get out and help her into the passenger seat beside him, so that she slammed the door closed with unnecessary violence as she took her place beside him.

His lean jaw clenched tightly for a moment, then he said as the car moved off down the cedar-lined driveway: 'I thought we might have lunch in town—is there a decent place to eat in Melville?'

'By "decent" I suppose you mean a place where pretty waitresses play Delilah to your Samson?' she said caustically. 'This isn't Texas with all those southern belles, you know!'

'I'd noticed that,' he said drily, and accomplished the remainder of the ten-mile drive in silence, a silence Abby was too stubborn to break. Why hadn't he stayed in Texas if he wanted simpering, clinging females—though, from what she had read and heard, there weren't many of those around the sun-baked ranches there. But, more to the point, why didn't Ben go back to his wife and let her fuss over him in the manner he was used to? This last thought brought her resentful eyes to the thin-faced profile presented to her.

He had taken off his hat and tossed it on the back seat so that his thick hair formed a partially tamed topping to the sweep of tanned forehead and well-formed nose over sensuously outlined lips and hard chin. A woman's dream, she mocked silently—so why hadn't the woman he had given his name to kept him by her side instead of letting him wander off to Texas and now to Cedar Hills Ranch?

'This seems the most likely place for lunch,' he said, politely conversationally as he parked in front of the Sage Hotel on Main Street. 'I'll meet you back here at one.'

'Thank you!' Abby said with pointed sarcasm, and thrust her slender legs from the car, coming upright just as Ben stretched his long body at the other side.

'You'll be here at one?'

'What else?' she mocked, and before he had time to register more than frowning disapproval she had skipped away from the car and was walking with quickly drumming heels down the unusually wide main street lined with stores and business offices.

She attended first to the shopping Harry had asked her to get, then lingered over the purchase of two shirt-blouses in the only department store of any size which the town boasted. Back on the main street, she sauntered lazily along the sidewalk, glancing in shop windows to pass the time until her lunch date with Ben—though date was hardly the word, she thought resentfully as she paused outside a small but exclusive dress shop run by a friend's sister. As if he was the boss and she the employee, his invitation had been more of a command than anything else. Her eyes wandered idly over the chic dresses displayed in the shop window, seeing yet not seeing the gossamer froth of chiffon mingling with the more severe lines of tailored suits and dresses in eye-catching colours.

'Abby! What are you doing in town?'

Abby started from her reverie and swung round to meet the dancing dark eyes of her friend, Debby Warner. It was Debby's sister Verna who owned the dress shop, and Debby

had given up her job at the department store to help her
sister become established.

'Oh, I had some shopping to do, and our new man was
coming in, so I came with him.'

'Mm. I heard you'd fired Dave—honestly, Abby, I don't
know how you have the nerve to do things like that! I mean,
I could never come right out and fire a man like Dave
Corben.'

'It wasn't too hard,' Abby returned briefly, her eyes taking in Debby's smart-looking pants suit in pale lime green
which contrasted attractively with her dark hair and slightly
olive skin. Obviously, Verna had begun to influence her
sister's choice of clothes since her return to Melville. Until
then, Debby's appearance had closely resembled Abby's,
her entire wardrobe away from work seeming to consist of
jeans and casual shirts. When she made a remark on those
lines, Debby said:

'Oh, Verna's been making me over, says I should show a
little taste now that my sister's bringing *haute couture* to
Melville.'

'How is the store doing?'

'Picking up a little now,' Debby confided with a faint
shrug. 'But it hasn't been easy for Verna trying to bring a
touch of class to women who've always bought mass-
produced things at Hanley's.'

Abby surreptitiously lowered her Hanley's bag behind her
leg, marvelling at the same time at Debby's changed ideas.
But then it was only to be expected that she would support
her own sister, she supposed.

'Is—is Verna's divorce through yet?'

'Any day now. Sometimes I wonder if she regrets leaving
Darrel, but she says not.' Debby's face took on an animated
look. 'Say, I'm glad I met you today, it's saved me a trip
out to your place—you're never around when I phone.'

'A ranch can't be run from a kitchen, you know,' Abby
observed drily. 'Anyway, what did you want to see me
about?'

'We're having a party at the house on Saturday night, and
naturally you're invited.' Debby's olive skin took on deeper
colour. 'Al Smith's coming—remember him from school?

He's been working down south for quite a while, but he's back here to stay now.'

'Oh.' An unaccountable pang shot through Abby at her friend's more than palpable interest in Al Smith, a gangly boy when he had hung around her at high school.

'Isn't there anybody you can bring?' Debby asked impulsively, something like compassion in her eyes for the friend who, although there had been plenty of boys a year or two ago who would have been only to happy to fill Abby's bill, had shied away from any deep or lasting relationships with any of them.

'Not really, but if it's a couples only party I won't embarrass you by coming.'

Sensing the hurt in Abby's voice, Debby quickly assured her: 'No, of course it's not couples only. As you know, there're a lot more unattached males than females around here, so you'll be welcomed with open arms.'

Abby glanced at the big watch on her wrist. 'Thanks. I really have to rush, Debby, I'm meeting Ben Franklin at the hotel at one.'

Debby's face registered comic disbelief. 'Ben Franklin? You have to be joking—nobody has a name like that!'

'His mother was an American and called all her sons after prominent Americans.'

'Oh, well, everyone to her taste!' Debby thrust an arm through Abby's. 'I'll walk part of the way with you. It's been ages since I saw you and there's so much I have to tell you.'

It hadn't been that long, Abby said silently, but she let her friend's chatter flow over her in a comforting stream. They had been intimates for so long that Debby's infatuation with Al Smith was as transparent as clear plastic as she brought his name into the conversation several times in the space of two short blocks.

'Wow! Who's that, honey?'

Abby was brought to an abrupt standstill and she angled her gaze in the same direction as Debby's, seeing Ben Franklin's tall figure emerging from the bank, one lean brown hand tucking papers into the breast pocket of his shirt.

'Oh, that's the new man,' she said casually, adding with a smile to her friend's engrossed expression: 'Ben Franklin.'

'He's beautiful,' Debby breathed. 'Abby, how can you possibly work with a man like that and not fall madly in love with him? He's absolute perfection!'

'There's more to him than meets the eye,' Abby was saying darkly when Debby cut across her words, obviously not hearing them.

'You'll have to bring him with you on Saturday night, Abby,' she said urgently. 'Even if you're not interested, he'd be just the one to shake Verna out of her half regrets about Darrel! Come on, let's catch up with him and I'll ask him right now.'

'But he's——' Abby began, but bit back the words as her friend pulled her firmly after the broad-shouldered figure with the flat narrow hips that even from a distance gave off an air of assured masculinity. She couldn't even tell Debby that Ben Franklin was married ... her impulsive friend was more than likely to ask something about his wife, and he would know immediately that Abby had listened in to his conversation.

The light green eyes turned and recognised Abby when they came abreast of him and he stopped, lifting his hat as Abby introduced her friend a shade curtly.

'I've just been saying to Abby that she should bring you to our party on Saturday,' Debby burbled, obviously impressed with Ben's good looks as he bent his attention on her. 'As you're a stranger in the community, it would be a good chance for you to meet some of the people.'

Ben smiled uninhibitedly into her eager face, and Abby heard her swift intake of breath. 'That's very kind of you, Miss Warner, and I'd appreciate the chance to meet a few of the townsfolk.' His gaze narrowed on Abby. 'I've only met Cedar Hills ranch people so far.'

'Then we'll expect you around eight on Saturday night,' Debby agreed breathlessly, not taking her eyes from Ben even when he tipped his hat and put a hand under Abby's arm to lead her to the hotel half a block away. 'Best bib and tucker, Abby!' she called laughingly after them, and Abby turned to raise her brows, a frown settling between them when she saw Debby's hands pressed to her heart and eyes raised heavenwards in an eloquent gesture.

'Don't you want me to escort you to your friend's party?' Ben asked with a sideways glance at her stormy countenance, his hand on her arm sending uncomfortable sensations through it.

'It doesn't matter to me either way,' she returned snappishly, wondering how he could contemplate enjoying himself at a party while his wife languished somewhere far away.

'Good,' he said equably. 'It promises to be a happy evening.'

CHAPTER THREE

THE promise of a happy evening seemed remote, however, when Abby opened the door to Ben on Saturday at seven-thirty and saw his eyes go questioningly, and somewhat insultingly, over her outfit of navy slacks and floral blouse in shades of blue on a white background.

'I'm sorry,' he said, 'am I too early?'

'Too early for what?'

'For you to have changed into your party clothes,' he explained shortly. His own immaculate good looks in dark grey suit and lighter grey shirt with tie to match sent her pulses racing unforgivably, but her chin lifted defiantly.

'I *am* dressed for the party,' she told him icily. 'Parties at the Warners are never dress-up affairs, you know,' she sent her glance scathingly over his perfectly turned out appearance.

'I thought your friend said "best bib and tucker",' countered Ben, his eyes hardening.

'To Debby, that means my best slacks—which these are —and newest top—which this is!'

Their eyes locked for a dangerous moment, then Ben gave a resigned shrug, but Abby sensed the quiet anger in him as he followed her to the car, letting her seat herself in the passenger seat while he took his place behind the wheel.

The journey was once more accomplished in silence, a strained atmosphere that kept Abby quietly fulminating beside Ben's tautly held body as he manoeuvred the wheel with competent brown hands. She was clean, wasn't she? . . . fresh from the shower with her hair brushed to gleaming softness, her skin clear apart from a few freckles here and there . . . even her mouth brushed lightly with the lipstick she seldom used. Had he expected her to appear in one of those gossamer-fine creations in Verna's shop window? This thought leavened her mood and a smile lit across her lips when she imagined Debby's face if she had turned up in one of those.

But it was her own face that fell when she saw Debby in a swirling tawny-coloured dress and make-up which made her oldest friend look like a stranger to her. Debby's half-dismayed glance over Abby's slacks and top wasn't lost on her either, and she was relieved to see that some of the younger guests were even more casually attired than herself.

'Dave's here,' Debby hissed dramatically in Abby's ear, unnecessary as it happened because Dave's big blond figure appeared behind her shoulder at that moment.

He smiled tightly. 'Hi, Abby,' he said, barely glancing at Ben, who was smiling with equal restraint into Debby's excited face raised to his as she slipped an arm through his and drew him away. 'I want to talk to you.' Without further ado, Dave put an arm round Abby and shepherded her over to a shaded corner at one side of the patio where people were already gathered for dancing to a record player. A glance back showed Abby that Ben was being led, not unwillingly, to where Verna had just appeared outside the patio doors. Dressed dramatically in calf-length white lace which showed the dark-hued skin to perfection, Debby's sister gave Ben a dazzling smile when the younger girl made the introduction.

'What is it, Dave?' Abby asked with a stab of bored anger as Dave tightened his grip on her arm to turn her round to face him. Her eyes took in with distaste the light film of sweat beading his fair-skinned brow, the glowering blue of his light coloured eyes as they fastened on her face.

'You know damn well what it is, Abby,' he ground out, his fingers gouging the soft flesh of her arm. 'I'm giving you one last chance to get rid of that roving cowboy Romeo over there and put me back where I belong.'

'As it happens,' she replied coolly, 'that cowboy Romeo is doing just fine.' Her defence of Ben surprised even herself, but she knew it was justified when she looked up into Dave's arrogantly aggressive face.

'So I hear,' he sneered, 'with you!'

Abby's cheeks flamed bright with colour and her eyes dropped momentarily from the deliberate taunt in Dave's. It was inevitable, she supposed, that young Joe had regaled the rest of the men with what he had seen in Ben's bungalow and that Walt, Dave's crony, had kept him up to date with ranch matters.

'So?' her brows arched. 'He tried to get fresh, and I put him in his place.'

Dave's head turned towards the patio, where several couples were dancing.

'I'm glad you feel that way about it, because it seems he's hitched himself to Verna for the evening—and I'd hate you to get hurt,' he added with mock commiseration.

Abby's head turned automatically in the same direction, and an unfamiliar hand squeezed her stomach muscles when she saw Ben's hand, brown and lean, on the white lace of Verna's dress, his eyes smiling bemusedly down into the excited glitter of hers. Come to think of it, she had never seen Verna quite so vivacious as now, her piquantly dark face framed with jet black hair that cascaded over her bare shoulders.

'Why would I get hurt?' she asked jerkily, turning back to Dave. 'All I'm concerned about is that Ben Franklin is good at his job—which he is.'

'You don't know anything about him—where he comes from, what he did before he came here.'

He worked on a ranch in Texas,' Abby informed him disdainfully. 'The owner trusted him enough to let him run the place for him.'

'And what happened?' Dave asked caustically. 'Why isn't he still there?'

'Be-because the owner died and his son decided to sell out.'

'So he tells you,' the ex-foreman scoffed. 'But I'd like to bet the owner would tell a different tale. Anybody who has nothing to hide would be more open about his past, Abby.'

Her troubled dark violet eyes met and glanced off his. Pointless to ask how he knew that Ben preserved an aura of secrecy about his past—probably Dave knew before she herself did the inevitable speculations of the ranch hands at Cedar Hills.

'As far as I'm concerned, he's doing a good job and that's all I'm interested in,' she said coolly at last. 'His—past is none of my concern.'

'For God's sake, Abby, get rid of him,' Dave urged fiercely. 'Trust me as your father did—I have a feeling you'll regret taking on this Franklin.'

Abby's head lifted so that her eyes looked clearly into his. 'My father's judgment was to trust in you. Mine is to trust in Ben Franklin.'

Dave's face registered livid anger, and the brutal dig of his fingers into the soft flesh of her upper arms seared through the fine material of her blouse.

'You'll be sorry you didn't listen to me,' he gritted. 'Don't come crying to me when you find out he's not worth the faith you've put in him.'

'Don't worry,' she blazed contemptuously. 'You'd be the last person I'd crawl to for any kind of help! And let me go!'

Neither of them noticed Ben's silent approach from the patio until his quietly controlled voice said at her side: 'You promised me a dance, Abby ... this seems as good a time as any.'

The two men measured each other with their eyes, and it was finally Dave who backed down from the bland menace in the ice green of Ben's. Cursing under his breath, he pushed Abby away from him so that she half fell into Ben's arms, which lifted automatically to receive her before pulling her against his firm body. Dave whirled round and stalked towards the front of the house, his heavy shoulders rigid with anger.

Ben waited until their steps had blended together on the patio to the sounds of a slow number before speaking. 'What was all that about?' he asked quietly.

For the space of several moments Abby was unable to answer him. Her stomach was churning after the scene with Dave, and added to that she had become unwillingly conscious of Ben's closeness, the heady male scent of him and the comforting strength of his arm circling her. She swallowed convulsively and blinked unexpected tears from her eyes with irritated jerkiness.

His arm tightened round her and she felt his chin brush the soft red-gold of her hair. 'But I guess I don't have to ask that, do I? He wanted you to get rid of me and take him back, right?'

Abby nodded wordlessly, her eyes fixed on his brown neck above the neat knot in his tie.

'Is that what you want to do?'

'No!' she found her voice and sent it out forcefully. 'No man—least of all Dave Corben—tells me what to do!'

Her head was thrown back as she spoke, and she saw the sudden clenching of Ben's lean jaw, the glint in the light eyes he bent on her.

'But one day you're going to have to let him or some other man tame that unfeminine streak in your make-up,' he told her tersely, his eyes narrowing as they went over the indignant pinkness on her face. 'As I said before, it might be worth my while to take up that challenge.'

'It would take a bigger man than you to do that!' she jeered, facing him with defiant hands on hips when the music stopped and he released her.

'Maybe you should take another look at Corben, then,' he snapped coldly. 'At least he's made a start by getting you to shed a few feminine tears! It might be better to leave you to him at that.'

'Yes, do that,' she returned sweetly. 'At least he's not——' She caught the remainder of the words in her throat, her eyes flickering nervously at the thought that she had nearly given away her knowledge that he was married.

'He's not—what, exactly?'

'He's not'—she searched frantically for substitute words and her eyes fell on Verna's slender figure in white lace as she laughed up into another man's face—'he's not hung up on feminine frills and fancies.'

'That's obvious,' he agreed, his eyes going insultingly over her own severely cut garb. 'He has the advantage of me there—I prefer women who look like women at least some of the time, and not like undersized teenage boys!'

Her mouth still hung open in chagrined amazement when

he had inclined his head very slightly and turned his back on her to cross to where Verna greeted him with undisguised pleasure. Nausea fought for control over the lump in Abby's throat, and she turned away blindly when Ben took Verna into his arms to dance, his cheek coming to rest on the glossy cloud of her dark hair as they moved round the patio.

The Warner house was almost as familiar to her as her own, and she made her way instinctively to the small den at the front, knowing she would be undisturbed there. A dismayed gasp parted her lips when a couple, closely entwined on the sofa along the far wall, looked up at her with bemused faces. The colour running up under Al Smith's face was only slightly darker than Debby's. Muttering an apology, Abby escaped from the room and found herself back on the patio before she realised where her steps were taking her, and her acceptance of a dance from one of the men she had known since childhood was purely automatic.

That dance was followed by others with a variety of partners, but she seemed to move through a daze of conflicting thoughts. Uppermost was a sense of betrayal that Debby, who had shared her antipathy to male domination in her life, had gone over to the enemy without a backward look. Long before the food was served, Abby wished that she could go home—or, better still, that she had never come.

Ben evidently had no such regrets, giving every sign of enjoying himself with Verna, his green-eyed gaze resting only occasionally on Abby, and then with an impersonality she told herself didn't matter one bit.

It was after eleven when he came across to where she stood with a group of old friends reminiscing about familiar and sometimes hilarious incidents from their common past. Aware that he waited on the outer edge of the group, Abby leaned further into it and pretended absorption in the laughing tale which Clint Edwards, the handsome son of a neighbouring rancher, was getting out with difficulty. Suddenly she felt a cool grasp on her arm and heard Ben's quiet:

'Sorry to break it up, Abby, but it's time we went home.'

There was a sudden silence as everyone in the group looked at the tall stranger and his possessive hand on Abby's arm, then exchanged embarrassed looks as if wondering whether they should do something about this encroachment on their charmed circle.

'In a few minutes, Ben,' Abby returned with a forced coolness which she congratulated herself on because her blood was boiling over in her veins.

'*Now*, Abby,' he insisted, pulling her resisting body from between two of the men who looked suddenly like callow boys in comparison to his steely-eyed assurance. Perhaps it was because of this unquestionable air of confidence that the others only murmured their goodnights as Ben bore Abby off to thank their host and hostess before escorting her to the station wagon parked close to the house.

She waited until he had set the car in motion and executed a U-turn on the street before giving vent to her pent-up feelings.

'How dare you take such a high-handed attitude with me, Ben Franklin?' she fumed.

'Because I was ready to leave,' he answered with implacable mildness.

'Then why didn't you? There were plenty of others who would have driven me home.'

'I wasn't exactly deafened by offers,' he observed drily, and accurately. 'Anyway, I brought you and it's my place to take you home. You see, all my mother's training didn't go to waste. She always told me——'

'I don't give a darn what your mother told you,' she muttered, quieter but no less venomous. 'If I'd met her I'd have given her my sincere condolences on giving birth to a son like you.'

Unperturbed, he glanced across at her with an amused, barely discernible smile. Ignoring the last part of her sentence, he said as his eyes turned back to the road illuminated by powerful headlights: 'That would have been quite a meeting! You're similar types ... in looks, but more so in character.'

'What's that supposed to mean?' she asked suspiciously, intrigued in spite of herself.

She saw his shoulders lift in a faint shrug and the faint glint of his teeth as his smile broadened.

'She was determined, too, that no man would ever tame her ... until my father came along and persuaded her otherwise.'

Abby digested this for several moments, then erased a softer note from her voice when she said : 'And how do you know she didn't hate every minute of being forced into conforming to a man's wishes?'

The thought crossed her mind, when he took so long to answer, that she had offended him by suggesting that his mother had been unhappy in her marriage, but at last he spoke, a gentleness in his voice that had been missing before.

'Because she never made any effort to hide what she felt for my father, any more than he masked his feelings for her. I've always thought their love was stronger because of the initial—difficulties.'

Unbidden images raised themselves before Abby's eyes ... of a love-filled home where a man and woman rejoiced in each other and the children their love had created.

'My mother died when I was five,' she said, subdued as she gave an unconscious sigh. 'I hardly remember her, and Dad never found it easy to talk about her.'

His head turned to her momentarily, the expression in his eyes obscured when he said : 'I can understand that. I'd find it hard to talk about my wife if——' He broke off and his hands tightened on the wheel, his knuckles showing white in the moonlight that slanted through the windscreen.

You find it difficult to talk about your wife anyway, Abby said tartly, and silently, her mood of pleasant sentiment gone. What kind of man was he to go around kissing a girl he hardly knew—and her his boss to boot!—and flirt with an obviously enamoured Verna for a whole evening?

'I doubt if you'd find anything hard to do,' she threw at him bitterly, and saw the surprised jerk of his head and the raking inspection of his eyes over her face before an impatient sigh escaped him.

'Why are you stopping?' she asked, alarmed when he drew the car suddenly to the side of the road and braked violently, throwing her forward so that her hands came up to press against the dashboard.

'I'm stopping because I can't do two things at once,' he ground out with savage forcefulness. 'Namely, drive the car *and* stop that witchy tongue of yours for at least a few minutes!'

Fear licked along her veins when his hands, lean and bitingly hard, grasped her shoulders and turned her body to meet the instant impact of his as he slid along the seat and pinned her helplessly against the door, the handle feeling like a blunt-edged sword in the small of her back. The moon's silvery glow served to emphasise the diamond-hard glitter in the opaque eyes as they looked challengingly into hers for a moment or two before his head bent to the quivering fullness of her parted lips.

'Don't!' she half pleaded, half commanded, but it was as if she had proffered an invitation instead. Swiftly, breath-takingly, his mouth came down to cover hers and shock held her rigid while the warm firmness of his lips, devouring in their intensity, silenced her with deadly effectiveness. Her mind grew numb, her world bounded only by the driving force of the revenge he extracted, her vision filled only with the outline of his dark red head bent over hers.

Then as suddenly as the icy assault had begun, the quality of his kiss changed and became more persistently demanding of a response from Abby's inert form. She scarcely missed the hard pressure of the door handle on her back when Ben gathered her closer to the blazing heat of his body and ran an urgent hand from her shoulder to her thigh before coming up to slide under the flimsy covering of her blouse and sear the softness of her bare flesh with its rough-skinned warmth. Her senses reeled out of her control as her eyes closed and her mouth obeyed the impulses originating deep within her ... primitive impulses she had only guessed at, but which now took over from her inhibited surface and initiated the movement that drew his head down again to hers when he lifted it fractionally away. Her lips moulded themselves to the contour of his, and her hands twisted in the rumpled thickness of his hair, the long-delayed arousal of her woman's instinct to complement the male's driving desire for fulfilment igniting the dormant part of her being and spreading like wildfire ... flame that leapt from her newly sensitised lips to the outermost tips of her toes, which curled reflexively in her blue-toned shoes.

'Abby ... Abby,' he groaned close to her ear, his mouth then tracing a fiery trail along her jaw and down to the madly activated pulse on her throat before descending to the invitingly warm softness between the inexplicably opened top buttons of her blouse.

And while her drowning senses saw again the plateau and steep-sided mountain of the other time Ben had kissed her, a nagging thought took wing and fluttered persistently at the back of her mind. Even to her inexperienced senses, his lovemaking bore the touch of an expert, of a man well used to rousing a woman physically until she responded in just the way he wanted ... and why not? He had a wife ...

Abby stiffened and turned her head away when he lifted his to look questioningly at her. 'What's wrong, Abby?' he asked, quietly husky, his fingers gently fastening on her chin to turn her face back to his. 'Am I going too fast?'

Her breath came in little pants as her eyes glinted feverishly off the moon-coolness of his. 'Sylvia might think so,' she said, her voice brittle, and felt the immediate tensing of his muscles.

'Sylvia? What do you know about Sylvia?' His eyes had lost their lazily sensuous look and were warily alert as they stared directly into Abby's. Even his breathing had steadied suddenly as he waited for the answer she found herself incapable of giving. Something about the way her lashes swept down over her eyes to avoid his penetrating stare, the defiant outthrust of her lower lip, sent a light of understanding into his eyes. 'Oh, I see,' he said softly. 'You listened in to my phone conversation that first night.'

'I had a right to know more about you than you'd told me!'

His mouth drew into a taut line and a furrow appeared between his brows in the ensuing silence. At last he said quietly: 'How much of that conversation did you hear?'

'Enough to know that you have a wife and children somewhere who were expecting you home, but you came here instead.' Memories of his kisses, and her own reaction to them, prompted her to add scathingly: 'She has all my sympathy, being married to a man like you.'

'You can save your sympathy,' he returned coldly, lever-ing his long body away from her and sliding back behind the wheel. 'Sylvia's not married to me. She's my brother's wife.'

Abby's swift indrawn breath sounded loud in the quiet-ness of the car, her eyes swivelling round to the stony and somehow bleak look in his as he stared out to the front.

'But you love her, don't you?' Pain clutched at a hollow place inside her when his fingers tightened on the wheel.

'Yes, I love her,' he admitted with a deep drawn sigh. His eyes turned to flicker over the pale oval of her face. 'But it's the kind of love you wouldn't understand.'

That might have been true before he had come on the scene, Abby thought resentfully, pulling her eyes away from his face to direct them out to the moonlit meadows to their right. But now he had stirred emotions in her that had never before cried out for expression ... emotions she would far rather have left buried than have brought to life by a man who was in love with another woman.

'That—that's why you keep travelling around, isn't it?'

'Is it? You seem to have it all worked out in that narrow little mind of yours, so it's pointless for me to confirm or deny anything. You wouldn't believe me, would you?'

'Probably not—and I do not have a narrow little mind!'

His hand went to the ignition key on the dash and the engine sprang to life, running smoothly as he turned to say icily: 'Any mind that could accept that I'd be sitting in this car making love to you while I had a wife—*and* children, I believe you said!—waiting anxiously for me at home has to be narrow. To put it kindly!' The glittering slits of his eyes went contemptuously over her face. 'For a girl who thought I was a married lecher, you sure didn't put up much resistance either time I kissed you.'

Fast though her hand was to rise, his was even quicker, and she let out a gasp of pain as his fingers clamped with bloodstopping fierceness on her wrist. Blue eyes clashed angrily with light green in silent battle until Abby ground out:

'You didn't give me much of a chance to resist either time, did you?'

Ben's laugh was hard as he threw her hand down on her lap. 'Don't come the ravaged maiden with me, Abby! A man knows when a woman's willing, and once you warmed up you were more than willing! And don't try slapping my face again,' he warned frostily, 'or I'll be tempted to give you something your father should have a few years ago!'

'A typical male response,' she jibed, the effect diminished because of the breathless catch in her voice. 'Brute force will get you anywhere! Well, maybe your Sylvia likes the he-man approach—and I know Verna does!—so why don't you concentrate your efforts on them?'

'Maybe I'll do that!' he snapped, and set the car into motion with a violent wrench at the wheel that made gravel chips fly up noisily under the tires. 'Either one of them could teach you a thing or two about femininity!'

Abby disdained a reply to that and sat in frozen silence the rest of the way home and rushed out of the car before Ben could move from his seat, which she knew he hadn't intended to do anyway. No sooner had she slammed the door than the wheels crunched grittily off to the far end of the parking area.

Harry had left the outside porch light on as well as the small night light in the hall, and Abby guessed from the quietness prevailing in the house that Harry and Phil had retired to their room at the back of the house. They had moved in there when the last of their children had left home, and Abby had been more than glad of their company after her father's death. Quietly, so that she would not disturb them, she moved along the passage to her bedroom. The familiar room sprang to life when she flicked the light switch, which was also connected to twin rose-shaded lamps at either side of the single bed.

Everything about the room was designed to give an air of plain but cosy warmth, from the honey-toned maple furniture to the white candlewick bedspread and curtains in pink sprigged cotton. The wall-to-wall carpet was of solid deep pink and of a thickness that invited barefoot walking.

But now a shiver ran over Abby's spine, a coldness that came not from the room but from some apprehension deep inside her. A loneliness she had not known even at her father's death encircled her, and the tears she had been holding back in the car welled into her eyes as she crossed dejectedly to a padded basket chair near the window and dropped into it.

Years of such loneliness stretched before her mind's eye in never-ending line, a solitariness she had never even contemplated in any detail until Ben Franklin's overpoweringly male influence had entered her life. She had supposed that somewhere in the distant future there would be a man and that she would marry him, but love was a misty quality she had never spared much thought for in a personal sense.

Until now ... was she imagining herself in love with Ben Franklin on the strength of two kissing sessions, which in his experienced hands had lit the smouldering fires of sexual passion in her? No. He was the epitome of all she detested in men ... arrogant, confidently superior in his attitudes, secure in his world where women were mere appendages of men and designed for their comfort.

Abby rose suddenly and crossed to take a paper tissue from the box by her bed, her eyes drawn almost unwillingly to the dressing table mirror where she found herself a moment later contemplating the slender lines of her figure in blouse and slacks. Neat, trim, clean-cut—and far removed from Verna's completely feminine appearance earlier. Abby's ruthless eyes suddenly saw herself as Ben had seen her, and she knew why he had likened her to a boy. Yet he had kissed her as if she was desirable to him as a woman ... or had he? Was it Abby Mackenzie he held in a passionate embrace?... or was it the memory of Sylvia, his brother's wife, evoked by Verna's ultra-feminine company all evening?

In a frenzy of hurt, Abby stripped off the clothes that were all at once offensive to her and sped to her chest of drawers to extract a flimsily extravagant nightdress an unmet aunt in Scotland had sent to her for Christmas, one she had never worn. The whisper soft folds of creamy nylon settled like a caress round her slenderly curved body and moved sensuously against her skin as she returned to the mirror.

Picking up her hairbrush, she stroked the light red-gold strands to a glimmering cloud, standing back to gauge the effect and knowing with catching breath that feminine allure was hers in plenty ... gold-tinted skin gleamed softly and partly shaded through the silk-like layers, lips still warmly full from Ben's kisses needed no artificial aids to colour them, eyes with the dark dewy freshness of violets, and hair which other women unsuccessfully spent a fortune trying to emulate—all these were hers, but her mouth trembled and her shoulders slumped under the wispy swathe of gossamer material.

Ben Franklin would never see her like this ...

CHAPTER FOUR

'DID you enjoy the party?'

Harry's cheerful voice for once struck a wrong note on Abby's ears when she took her place for breakfast in the sunny kitchen alcove next morning.

'It was all right,' she shrugged. 'Debby's out of her skull over Al Smith, so I hardly saw her all evening.'

Harry gave her a shrewd look before saying matter-of-factly: 'Well, that's only natural, isn't it? Sooner or later she was bound to fall, and she's about twenty-two years old, isn't she?'

'She's the same age as me, as you well know,' Abby pointed out sharply. 'I can't for the life of me think what she sees in Al—he hasn't improved a whole lot since high school.'

'Not to you, maybe,' Harry returned comfortably. 'But Debby sees things in him that you can't, I've no doubt.' When Abby made no reply, she went on: 'How did you get along with Ben?'

'I didn't,' the girl told her briefly, taking a gulp of the strong black coffee Harry had put before her. 'He spent most of the evening with Verna, and she fastened on to him as if she'd never heard of a husband in Vancouver.'

'Well,' the housekeeper sighed, 'he's an attractive man, as I've said before. And I guess Verna's divorce is just about through, isn't it?'

'Any day now,' Abby repeated Debby's words gloomily. 'She's just the type Ben likes, all female and big-eyed, hanging on every word he condescends to speak.'

'Mmm. Most men seem to go for women who need a strong arm for support.' Harry put Abby's breakfast of crisply fried bacon and eggs before her. 'Even Phil's like that.'

53

'*Phil?*'

'Oh, yes,' the older woman laughed, temporarily taking a seat opposite Abby. 'There's lots of things I could do myself without too much trouble, but I ask him to do them because it makes him feel strong and protective.'

'But that's cheating, Harry!' Abby said indignantly, her breakfast forgotten as she stared with fiery eyes across the table into the housekeeper's complacent face. 'How can he respect you as a person if you——'

'Respect?' Harry shrugged. 'That comes as part of loving, I guess, and Phil loves me because I let him be the man in the family.'

She rose, her eyes lighting up when the back door opened and the man in her family came in bearing an unplucked and very dead chicken in one hand. Phil, with his lined and weatherbeaten face, was as familiar and dear to Abby as was Harry herself, and she exerted her facial muscles in a smile.

'Hi, Abby. Have a good time with your young man last night?'

'My——? Ben Franklin isn't my young man, Phil! Just because he drove me to the Warner party it doesn't make him anyone special.'

Phil chuckled. 'No, I guess it doesn't. And he sure doesn't look like a man who's spent the evening with his dream girl this morning. Snapping everybody's head off down in the horse barn.' He turned to his wife. 'Want me to pluck this for you, Harriet?'

'Please, honey. You know I don't like handling feathers, and you make a much better job of it than I do.'

Abby gazed hard at Harry's blandly smiling face as Phil went happily from the kitchen. 'That was for my benefit, I suppose!'

'Why should you think that? Phil's been asking me that question for more than thirty-six years, and I've been giving him the same answer for that length of time.' Harry shrugged her ample shoulders and turned to the sink where the dishes were soaking. 'He just likes to hear me ask him to do it—I guess so that he'll know I'm not taking him for granted.'

'I give up.' Abby rose disgustedly from the table and

carried her dishes to the sink, where Harry took them from her and dumped them in beside the others.

'Are you going to be in for lunch today, or do you want sandwiches?'

'Mmm ...' Abby's brow wrinkled slightly. 'I'm not sure, Harry, I'll let you know later. I might ride up to the Mellon pasture and check how ready it is for cutting.'

'Ben going with you?'

'I don't know—why?' Abby looked suspiciously into the housekeeper's bland expression.

'No reason, except that I thought I could make you a picnic lunch. It should be lovely by the lake today.'

'So it should,' Abby snapped irritably, turning to the door, 'for those who have that kind of leisure. Ben Franklin doesn't happen to be one of them. He's paid to help me run the ranch, not idle his time away beside a lake!'

Harry's surprised look followed her out to the brilliance of early morning sunshine. Ben Franklin had really hit the mark with the housekeeper who had been the only mother Abby had known. Never before had Harry been at such obvious pains to match her up with a man, though she knew less about him than Abby did. But she would hardly throw them together if she still thought Ben was married, so he must have confided that much at least to her willing ears.

The frown ruffling her brow was reflected in Ben's scowling face when she found him five minutes later leaning on the corral fence moodily watching Joe try his hand at breaking in a restless young horse. He turned from the enclosure as Abby came up quietly to stand beside him, dipping his head briefly in acknowledgement of her presence, his eyes flickering expressionlessly over her pale yellow shirt and hip-hugging jeans to her small booted feet before turning back to watch Joe with narrow-eyed concentration.

An impatient exclamation came from him when the almost black colt jumped away again from the halter lead Joe was carrying round and raced away to the far corner of the corral. Putting one foot on the middle rail and one hand on the top, Ben vaulted the fence and went with an unhurried gait to pick up a coiled rope looped round one of the gateposts.

'We'll have to do it a different way,' he told the boy, his voice quiet but carrying. 'If we don't get him settled to a halter soon, he'll fight every time one comes near him in future.'

The small animal eyed the man's lithe figure warily as he circled closer, his arm raised to twirl the wide loop he had made on the rope's end. A split second before the loop arced towards him, the colt jumped and sprang away to the other side of the corral so that the rope thudded uselessly against the fence. Panicking when Ben came implacably back to the centre of the corral, the rope swinging again, the animal made a mad dash round the outer perimeter, to be brought up short on the next throw which sent the lariat over his head to settle snugly round his neck.

Speaking quietly and with hypnotic smoothness, Ben gradually worked his way along the rope until the colt was within reach. One hand held the rope taut while the other lifted to stroke soothingly across the glossy coat, the voice continuing on a coaxing note so that the horse stopped quivering and lifted his ears as if listening intently to the man's words. Finally, Ben lifted a hand without looking at Joe, and the boy immediately carried over the halter he had tried unsuccessfully to put on the horse.

Abby's breath was expelled in an explosive sigh a few moments later when Ben had settled the halter on the colt's head and tied the lariat rope firmly to the fence, giving the animal a few more strokes before turning to Joe.

'Leave him tied up there for a while till he gets used to the idea. Then you can try it again.'

'Thanks, Ben,' said Joe, his eyes shining with admiration as he watched the slim-hipped foreman use the gate this time to rejoin Abby.

'You've had a lot of experience at this, haven't you?' she asked, squinting slightly against the sun as she looked up into Ben's face.

'Some,' he conceded laconically, then surprised her by taking her elbow and leading her away from the corral. 'Last night——'

'It doesn't matter,' Abby put in hurriedly. 'I've forgotten about it already.'

Ben halted and looked down at her, a faintly sardonic smile touching one corner of his mouth. 'Have you? At another time, I might argue that point with you, but that wasn't what I was talking about.'

'Oh.' Deflated, Abby felt hotness bathe her neck and cheeks and she turned away to hide her embarrassment from him.

'Did you hear anything last night after you went to bed?' he went on, the smile disappearing as his mouth tightened.

'Hear anything?' She looked back at him, forgetting her discomfort of a moment before. 'What kind of thing?'

'A truck, about two o'clock this morning.'

Her brow knitted in a perplexed frown. 'No—*yes*! But it was just old man Henson's truck. He lives about five miles north of us, and he's been a little eccentric since his wife died a few years back. I asked Dave about it when I first heard the truck in the middle of the night—oh, three years ago, I guess, and he told me the old man had taken to shipping out his stock at odd hours of the night.'

'Corben told you that?' he asked sharply.

'Yes ... yes, it was Dave. He said not to worry about it.'

'I'll bet he did,' Ben said with ominous softness, biting his lip thoughtfully.

'What do you mean? Dave and I used to joke about the old man's peculiar ways, but——'

'It might have been a joke to you,' he returned grimly, 'but I doubt if it was to Corben.'

Bewildered, Abby stared up into his stonily unreadable face. 'You've lost me, long ago. Will you please tell me what you're talking about?'

He ignored that, however, instead taking her arm again and leading her firmly towards the office. 'I want to see your records for the past three years—you have them here?'

'Yes, but——' Belated indignation made Abby jerk her arm away from his hard grip and turn to face him belligerently. 'Don't you think you're taking on a lot more than your position warrants, Mr Franklin?'

Apart from a cooling of his eyes to ice green, Ben remained unperturbed as he stared down into the pink anger on her face. 'That's a matter of opinion, Miss Mackenzie. But with or without your permission, I'm going to examine those records.'

'And how are you proposing to get into a locked office?' she mocked, panting slightly as she half ran to keep up with his long, determined strides. 'Break in?'

'I don't think I'll have to do that,' he said evenly, turning to face her outside the office door. 'You carry the key on you, don't you?'

No sooner had his eyes dropped to the telltale outline in the breast pocket of her shirt than his hand reached out and dipped into it, his lean fingers searing the sharp rise of her soft flesh as they extracted the key.

'Now be a good girl and bring us some coffee,' he suggested calmly, inserting the key in the lock. 'It's likely to be a long morning.'

'Get it yourself!' she threw at his broad shoulders with impotent rudeness as he entered the sun-warmed room. 'I'm not your secretary.'

'Pity you're not,' he mused. 'You could have told me exactly where to find the books I'm looking for. As it is ...'

He strode over to the slatted shelves where the record books were stored and started to lift the green hardbacked books at random.

'The last three years' records are over here,' Abby bit off shortly, indicating the shelf behind her tautly held figure. 'But I'm not going to let you——'

'Oh, but you are going to let me,' he said firmly, coming across to lift her out of the way as if she weighed no more than a very small sack of grain. 'There's something strange going on here, and I want to know what it is.'

Ignoring her spluttering protests, he took down the books and spread them on the desk, lowering his long body into her own chair behind it and seeming to forget her presence as he flicked the pages over and studied the haphazard scrawls which were Abby's.

His absorption was total, and after a last venomous look at his thick brownish red hair bent over the desk, Abby went out fuming, spilling over to an astonished Harry in the hall of the house a moment later:

'Your Mr Franklin would like coffee in the office immediately—did you know that he's an accountant in disguise, Harry?'

'An—accountant?'

'You'll see for yourself when you take His Majesty's coffee!'

'Well, I ...' Harry looked faintly embarrassed as she held one arm to her ample bosom. 'I seem to have twisted my wrist somehow, Abby. Phil says it was when I turned mattresses this morning, but I don't know ... I can get the coffee, but will you carry the tray along to the office for me?'

It was on the tip of Abby's tongue to make a definite refusal, but a twinge of agony crossing the housekeeper's face as she bent to pick up a thread from a hall rug made her ask grudgingly: 'Is it that bad, Harry? Maybe you should see the doctor.'

'Oh, no, it's just a little sprain that resting will cure. It's happened before.'

'Well ... all right, I'll take the coffee in to him,' Abby conceded, and made no comment when the tray she collected ten minutes later contained two cups and a plateful of Harry's mouthwatering chocolate chip cookies.

As if he hadn't moved in the interval, Ben's head was still bent over the books spread on the desk, but there was a light of triumph in his eyes when she placed the tray on one corner and poured coffee for both of them.

'Thanks, Abby,' he said, his voice sincere as his white teeth bit into a cookie. 'This is good.'

'Harry made them,' she told him shortly, taking her own cup to the only other chair in the room and glaring resentfully at him, not liking the accepting nod of his head.

'Haven't you ever made cookies?' he asked conversationally, thrusting his tooled leather boots up on the desk and leaning back expansively in the chair.

'Only once,' she admitted frostily, recalling the disastrous effort which had produced a teeth-gluing concoction even her father had not been able to get down. A reluctant smile touched her lips and eyes. 'My father called them "Abby's secret weapon."'

The white surface of Ben's teeth showed in a commiserating smile. 'Mine to this day calls my first attempt to tame a horse "Ben's disaster"—so we have one thing in common.'

The friendly intimacy in his eyes made Abby cast hers down to the brown liquid in her cup. 'At least you've improved since then.'

'Practice brings a measure of perfection,' he said quietly, then his eyes strayed to the books beside him on the desk. 'I'm just part way through these records, Abby, but you seem to have had a lot of lost cows so far.'

'No more than the normal strays,' she defended warmly, forgetting for the moment that Ben Franklin was reaching beyond his authority in questioning the past conduct of the ranch. 'Dave always said it would cost more to put men to finding them than their market value was worth.'

'Mmm. Well, I'm not convinced of that,' he pronounced heavily, bring his feet down from the desk and angling his body closer to the inked pages before him. 'Last year, for instance, there's a discrepancy of fifty head—would you call that many "normal strays"?'

'Well, I ...' Abby hesitated, then, realising she was accepting his role of inquisitor, hardened her voice to say: 'Dave Corben knows the cattle business at least as well as you. My father—and *I*—trusted his judgment.'

'And I'm telling you now that your trust was very likely misplaced,' he returned grimly, long fingers beating a tattoo on the blue-lined pages.

'What are you suggesting?' Abby asked caustically. 'That Dave was spiriting away Cedar Hills stock for his own ends?'

'Exactly that.' Ben's voice was harsh, his eyes meeting hers in pinpoints of coldness. 'I think I'm going to uncover a systematic stealing of Cedar Hills cattle over the last three years at least.'

'What?' Abby stared at him in dumbstruck amazement. 'Dave wouldn't——'

'I think you'll find that Dave would,' he interjected drily. 'And not only would, but did.' His eyes came up to meet hers in an unblinking stare. 'Your father never mentioned that he suspected anything?'

'Of course not! Dad trusted Dave—even so far as to want me to——'

'Marry him?' Ben supplied coldly. 'Your father said to you that he'd like you to marry Corben?'

Abby frowned. 'Not in so many words, but Dave said——'

'You really did trust him, didn't you?' he jibed.

'Dad—liked Dave. He knew him a lot better than you ever will.'

'That's a thought I won't lose any sleep over,' Ben said with an expressive lift of his thick brows. 'Now, if you'll bring your chair round here, I'll show you what I mean.' His long body was on the move before he had finished speaking, and he took the heavy chair from her hands and carried it behind the desk for her.

'I'm quite capable of carrying a chair, for heaven's sake!' she said irritably, following him and looking belligerently into his eyes close to hers as he half straightened from setting the chair down.

'Just as I could have gone for coffee,' he smiled tightly. 'These are just little courtesies the sexes give one another.'

Uncomfortable with his nearness, Abby snapped: 'I only brought your coffee because Harry's hurt her wrist and couldn't carry the tray!'

A long-suffering sigh raised the taut muscles of his chest as he took the chair beside hers, but he made no further comment, his eyes immediately taking on a look of concentration as they fell on the opened record books before him.

'Now, let's see what else is missing ...'

Abby's skin had paled and her eyes were dark orbs of disgusted horror two hours later when she looked up into Ben's grim face.

'How could Dave have done this?' she whispered.

'It's not hard to take advantage of a sick man and a girl.' He rose suddenly and walked to the other side of the desk, taking one of the thin cigars he smoked from his breast pocket and striking a match viciously against the box. His eyes narrowed against the smoke curling up to his face as he looked at Abby when she spoke in a low voice.

'Thank heaven it was you who—discovered this.' A shudder ran over her. 'It might have been one of the Wests.'

'Did it never occur to you that the Wests might have been glad to help you?' his voice came clipped with cold anger. 'That they have a right to know what goes on here?'

'Their only right as far as Cedar Hills is concerned is to receive the quarterly payments on the loan, which they always do!'

'Not according to your father's will,' he shot back.

'Who told you about that?' she questioned suspiciously after a moment's silence.

'You did.' Ben turned away to open the door and stand in its place, blocking the light almost as effectively. 'It seems to me that if your father trusted the Wests enough to ask them to keep an eye on things, they can't be all that bad.'

'I didn't say they were bad,' she defended half sulkily. 'Just that they'd like nothing better than to come here and prove a girl can't run a ranch this size.'

'I happen to agree with them,' Ben looked over his shoulder to say, his eyes cool as they flickered over her well-formed but slight figure.

'You would!' she told him witheringly, coming from behind the desk to stand nearer to him, her hands on her hips in a familiarly aggressive stance. 'Why are you so much on the Wests' side anyway?'

'Because I don't like blind prejudice,' he said shortly, shifting his feet so that his lean form touched the doorframe and gave his eyes, their lids half closed, free access to her face. 'And that's what it is when you judge people before you've even met them.'

Abby's eyes fell before the censure in his, but only for

a moment. Lifting her head, she said firmly: 'Whether I'm being prejudiced or not, I intend to settle this thing with Dave without them ever finding out it happened.'

'And how do you propose to do that?'

'I'll—I'll talk to Dave, tell him I know what's been going on and warn him that ...'

Ben's laugh had a ring of genuine amusement in it. 'You'll scare him to death with those tactics,' he mocked, then his eyes sobered. 'No, Abby, you'd better leave it to me. I've worked out how to set a trap for him—and the others who help him.'

'How?'

He threw away the stub of his cigar on the gravelled forecourt outside and turned back into the room, closing the door behind him, then coming to half sit on the desk facing her, arms folded across his chest.

'By putting round the story that we're moving the cows out to summer pasture the day after tomorrow. There's no way he can get his truck up there, so he'll likely make a last stab while they're handy here ... probably tomorrow night, if my guess is right. And then we'll have him—or I should say the local police detachment will.' A satisfied smile touched the stern lines of his tightly held mouth.

'No!'

'What?'

'No police,' Abby said sharply. 'That means publicity, and the Wests might hear of it.'

'For God's sake, Abby, can't you forget your vendetta against the Wests for two minutes?' he demanded angrily. 'This man has been systematically stealing from Cedar Hills for three years or more, and all you can think of is the Wests!'

'Whether you like it or not, that's the way it is,' she maintained stubbornly. 'No police.'

Ben sighed exasperatedly and straightened away from the desk. 'Then I'll have to do it myself—and hope, like you, that he'll take a warning!'

'He will,' Abby returned with more confidence than she felt.

'I just hope you won't regret it,' he said resignedly as if tired of the whole subject, and went slowly back to the door.

'I won't.' She watched the broad back disappear through the hastily opened door, the set profile as it passed before the window. Sighing, she wandered to the seat he had occupied behind the desk, muttering beneath her breath as she slammed the record books shut and stared pensively at their green covers. Disquiet worked with apprehensive fingers along her spine and brought a frown between her eyes. Dave had an ugly temper when crossed; had she the right to expose Ben Franklin to possible danger because of her insistence that the police not be brought into it?

'*No!*'

Ben's adamant and whitely angry refusal later that afternoon sparked off a similar stab of anger in Abby.

'Either I come with you, or there'll be no lying in wait for Dave Corben or anybody else!'

'Don't be such a crazy little fool,' he growled in a voice several notches lower than its normal pitch. 'It won't be any place for a girl if Corben and his pals show up.'

'I'm not just any girl.' Abby pulled herself to her full height and stared at Ben's set face outlined against the barn door. 'Dave wouldn't do anything to harm me.' Or you, she added silently, if I'm there.

'No?' he asked sarcastically, a mirthless smile touching only his lips. 'If I'm right, that's exactly what he's been doing for years. Wouldn't you say that's odd behaviour for a man who says he wants to marry you?'

'I'm not responsible for what Dave and my father cooked up between them,' she snapped irritably. 'I was never consulted on whether I wanted to marry him or anyone else.'

Ben stared hard down into her eyes for a long moment, then capitulated with a suddenness that startled her. 'All right, you can come along,' he said, taut-lipped. 'On condition that you do exactly as I tell you.'

Abby opened her mouth to protest, but the grimly forceful expression on his face choked back the words before they had formed. 'Okay,' she said at last, relatively meek as she took a step back from him. 'You've set the word around that we're moving the cattle?'

He nodded. 'And as I expected, Wally left for town not long after, so we can expect another raid tonight or to-morrow night. My guess is that they'll have a stab at both nights, so I suggest that if you're coming tonight you have a rest for a while after supper. They won't come before midnight.'

Glory, the pregnant mare, heard their low-pitched voices and whinnied gently from within the barn. Abby's eyes moved from Ben's to the red barn door behind him.

'I'd better see to my horse now,' she said, standing back as he opened the big door for her.

'When is she due to foal?' he asked with polite interest.

'Any time now, and I think she's a little nervous.'

'That's understandable ... it's her first, isn't it?'

'Yes, but ...' Abby paused and bit her lip before going on into the barn and across to where the dark chestnut mare moved restlessly at the sound of her steps. 'She's more high-strung than I'd expected her to be.'

Ben had followed her to the horse's side and remarked drily as he ran expert hands over the mare: 'I guess you'll be high-strung, too, when you're this close to giving birth to your first child.'

Abby was glad that his absorption with Glory made him miss the sudden flame of colour in her cheeks, and she moved round to the horse's head to caress the short hairs between the animal's ears, murmuring incoherent nothings with an abstraction Glory seemed not to notice in her glad-ness at seeing her.

The sudden realisation sweeping over Abby and making her fingers tremble on Glory's finely shaped nose was that if and when she had her first child she would want a hus-band with Ben Franklin's gentle touch, his reassuring presence close by ... and that was such a ridiculous thought that she buried her face in the velvety soft muzzle and mocked her own fancies.

CHAPTER FIVE

COLD early morning air seemed to drip dampness from the surrounding bushes where Abby sat uncomfortably hugging her knees. She was cold, chilled to the bone, in spite of her compliance with Ben's instructions to wear warm clothing. The high-necked navy wool sweater and similarly coloured slacks had seemed more than adequate when she had first taken up her vigil, but now she stretched her cramped limbs and thought longingly of hot baths and coffee, and wondered if Ben was faring any better where he was.

He had left her at this spot on their arrival just before midnight, telling her in his most imperative tones to stay where she was, whatever happened. Then he had gone on ahead to take up a position out of sight behind a bank of hay sheds close to the railed-off pastures where the stock to be driven north to summer pastures moved restlessly as if sensing something in the air. Apart from the occasional fretful rumbling from them, only the intermittent hoot of a barn owl disturbed the moon-drenched silence.

Why hadn't she thought to bring flasks of coffee? Ben had warned her the night might be long and fruitless as far as a raid on the cattle was concerned.

The sudden low rumble of a truck's motor came from a far away stretch of the road behind Abby and she tensed her cramped muscles then half rose in a crouching position as the slowly driven truck approached and changed gear as it neared the entrance gate to Cedar Hills property. Abby saw that the headlights were switched off, the moon having been sufficient guide along the country road and now on the rough track over to the cattle pasture. One man had leapt from the truck when it paused at the outer gate, and two others remained in the cab as it passed thirty yards from where Abby hid. Too far away to identify the occupants apart from ascertaining that they were big men, one of whom could be Dave on the basis of size alone, but she couldn't be sure.

Three overpoweringly large men against Ben's solitary strength! And she had been the one to insist that he had no protection from the authorities who had jurisdiction over criminal activities such as these men were undertaking! Disregarding Ben's instructions to stay where she was, Abby jumped up and ran over the potholed ground to where the truck was turning and backing towards the gate entry into the pasture. If she could reach them before ... the breath was knocked from her body suddenly as her ankle twisted in a hole, sending her sprawling full length on the springy turf where new growth bushes whipped against her face with stinging slashes.

Scarcely aware of them, she scrambled to her feet and ran again, some kindly providence guiding her feet over the rough terrain until she burst into the clearing beside the hay sheds and drew to a panting halt as a big man's figure descended from the truck.

'Dave!'

'Good God!—Abby? What the hell are you doing here?'

'To stop you ... from taking ... any more cows,' she panted, crying out when Dave's big hand grasped her wrist and pulled her round so that her back was to him.

'Who put you up to this?' he gritted, tightening his grip so that she gasped again as needles of pain radiated from her wrist to her arm in concert with the shooting pain in her ankle. Even if she had wanted to answer, her closely pressed mouth, clamped against agony, would have prevented her.

'But I hardly need to ask that,' Dave went on harshly. 'It's your new boy-friend, isn't it? And where is he?' he added in a contemptuous tone as his head lifted to swivel round the area.

'I'm right here, Corben,' Ben's voice came from where he had stepped out from his shelter behind the hay sheds. 'Let her go!'

The steel in Ben's voice matched the dark grey of his

clothes, and Dave's grip momentarily slackened on Abby's
wrist, only to tighten again when Wally came panting up
from the outer gate.

'Get him, Wally!' Dave commanded harshly. 'You too,
Charlie,' he addressed the smaller, slimmer man who had
been driving the truck and who now circled Ben on his
right.

'Stop it!' Abby shouted. 'If you lay a hand on him, I'll
have the police out here before you know what hit you!'

As if she hadn't spoken, the two men continued to close
on Ben's tautly sprung figure and she closed her eyes, knowing as she succumbed to dizzying blackness that she was
responsible for Ben's death as well as her own ...

'Abby? Come on, Abby, wake up.'

An insistent tapping on her cheek brought Abby's
drugged senses to a hazy perception of coldness and a soft
light bathing her surroundings, throwing into relief the
man's harshly drawn features as they bent over her.

'Dave?' she whispered.

'He's gone,' the man's terse voice answered. 'You're safe
now, Abby.'

Not Dave—someone else who seemed to know her, but
the sharp-edged voice was unfamiliar ... yet she recognised
something in the shape of his face outlined against the
moon, the lift of thick hair over his temples ...

'Ben!' Without conscious volition, her body sat up
straight, eyes straining anxiously in the man's direction. 'Are
you—all right?'

'I'm fine, Abby,' he murmured, belying the dark bruise
high up on his cheekbone. 'Let's get away from here—can
you walk?'

'Of course I can walk!' she told him snappishly, resenting
the weakness that made her want to lay her head against
the hollow of his shoulder so close to her cheek.

He helped her to her feet, and she stepped away from
him, gritting her teeth against the sharp pains shooting from
ankle to calf in her left leg. Although she had made no
audible complaint, Ben swooped her off her feet and lifted
her high in his arms.

'I can walk,' she muttered.

'Oh, yes?' Ben strode purposefully towards the jeep he had parked out of sight under the trees some distance from the hay sheds and Abby made no further demur, giving herself up to the purely sensual pleasure of being carried in his firm-muscled arms which held her so close that she could feel the even rhythm of his heart against her breast. A wave of dizziness sent her mind into a whirl, and when her vision cleared again her head was resting in that hollow in his shoulder, her mouth a breath away from the strong column of his neck. So close was she that the masculine scent of his skin filled her nostrils, his breath warm on her face when he turned to glance down at her.

'Ben?' she whispered wonderingly.

'We're nearly there, Abby,' he said in a voice that was almost caressing and only a little louder than her own.

But strangely, she didn't mind if they never reached the vehicle ... didn't mind the idea of being carried for ever in those all-protecting arms ... nothing and no one could hurt her while Ben with his steady beating heart was there beside her ...

He took off the thick jacket he was wearing and made a pillow for her head on the rear seat, settling her there before getting behind the wheel himself and easing the jeep from under the sheltering trees, cursing softly under his breath when potholes under the wheels sent jolts through the jeep.

It was smoother going when they reached the road, and in minutes the driveway of Cedar Hills leapt to life in the headlights, which reflected back and outlined Ben's well-set head and shoulders. It was almost disappointing when he disappeared from view after drawing up in front of the house, but then she was in his arms again, being carried lightly into the house and across the hall in the dim light she had left on.

'Which room is yours?' he asked softly, evidently as reluctant as Abby to wake the still slumbering Harry and her husband at the rear of the house. Abby had thought it advisable to tell them nothing of her moonlight rendezvous with Ben. Phil would have insisted on going to Ben's aid, and Harry would have been equally insistent that Abby leave that kind of work to the men.

The room flooded with a pink glow when Abby reached behind Ben's shoulder for the light switch, and his eyes went quickly and assessingly round the room before striding with her to the bed and laying her on top of the covers.

'Let's have a look at that ankle first,' he said, his face set in grim lines as he turned and bent over her leg, but his fingers were incredibly gentle when he pulled back the cuff on her slacks and eased off her shoe, revealing a purplish swelling under a torn stocking. His mouth tightened to angry lines.

'Why didn't you stay put as I told you? Apart from ruining the whole expedition, you've got yourself a badly sprained ankle!'

'I did *not* ruin it,' she denied hotly, her temper flaring to match his as she stared up into the green fury of his eyes. 'I—I was trying to stop you from getting hurt.' She could do nothing to control the sudden and unexpected rush of tears to her eyes, the quiver that made her mouth tremble, and her head turned sharply away from his searing gaze.

'Abby,' he said gently after a few long moments of silence, and she felt his weight come down on the bed beside her, his fingers fastening on her chin to turn her face round to his. 'I'm sorry I jumped on you, but ... you could have been badly hurt tonight, and how do you think I'd have felt then? A man likes to think *he*'s doing the protecting ...' He sighed. 'I guess it was my fault for letting you come, I should have forbidden it.'

Like red rag to a bull, his words sent the flash of diamond chips into Abby's eyes and she pulled her chin free of his fingers, gasping when she tried to lift herself up and white-hot pains shot through her ankle and leg. '*You* forbid it? You haven't the right to forbid me anything, Ben Franklin!' She flopped back against the pillows again and panted: 'You keep forgetting that you—you're just an employee here and that *I* run Cedar Hills, not you!'

Ben sighed regretfully, rising and looking down at her with an odd expression in his eyes. 'You have a lot to learn, Abby.'

'Not from you!' she retorted promptly, then bit her lip at the unabated pain in her ankle.

'I'll have to do something about that ankle,' he said, turning to examine it cursorily again. 'You'll have to get undressed so that I can bandage it and hold the swelling.' Her indignant gasp brought his head round, a sardonic smile gleaming faintly far back in his eyes. 'If you tell me where you keep the very sensible pyjamas I'd bet you wear in bed, I'll get them for you and you can change while I see about a bandage.'

Pain was forgotten in the tide of embarrassed pique washing over her. Not for anything would she let Ben know that his bet would have been easily won until a few nights ago.

'My nightdress,' she stressed, 'is in the top bureau drawer over there.'

Giving her just a glimpse of eyebrows raised in surprise, he crossed to the dresser she indicated and opened the top drawer, hesitating before lifting out the cream nylon nightdress she had tried on for her own benefit, the gossamer folds seeming even more wispy in his big tanned hands. The one she had been sure he would never see her in.

'This?' he asked with insulting incredulity, holding it out full length and looking doubtfully from it to Abby and back again.

'What's wrong with it?'

'Not one thing,' he answered with appreciative slowness, coming to lay the nightdress at the foot of the bed, a smile tugging the corners of his mouth. 'But if I'm to keep my mind on bandaging the ankle, neck-high flannel pyjamas might be better.'

'I don't have any, I'm sorry,' she lied without compunction. 'You don't have to look at me.'

'That could be a point for debate,' he rejoined, and moved to the door. 'Where will I find the necessary?'

'In the kitchen. The cupboard to the left of the rear window has first aid supplies.'

Easing off the torn stocking over the puffy swelling on her ankle was an exercise in teeth-gritting skill, but she managed it at last and hopped with more jaw-clenching to the bathroom where she rinsed her face quickly, leaving only a few faint scratches visible where she had come into forceful contact with the bushes, and ran a brush through her hair, knowing that apart from the scratches, she looked as desirable as she had the last time she had worn the nightdress. Not that she cared a fig for what Ben Franklin thought of her personally, she told herself as she made her slowly painful way back to the bed. She just wanted him to know that she could look as feminine as anybody else when it suited her.

When Ben returned, an ice pack and sterile roll of bandage in one hand and a half-filled glass of amber liquid in the other, she was installed on the bed again with the covers pulled back, only a sheet covering her discreetly as far as just below her bared shoulders.

His eyes flickered once over shining hair and across her face to the creamy softness of her shoulders before he set the bandage and glass down on the bedside table and lifted the sheet away from her leg. Exclaiming softly at the purple discolouration, he disappeared into the bathroom to emerge a moment later with a thick bath towel, which he inserted under the leg before settling the ice pack round her ankle. Then he straightened to pick up the glass, fumes from it curling Abby's nose as he handed it to her.

'I don't like brandy,' she complained, moving her head so that the obnoxious odour wasn't so strong in her nostrils.

'I'm not asking you to like it,' he said tersely. 'I'm telling you to drink it! Or do I have to hold your nose and make you swallow it?'

About to refuse again, Abby caught sight of the tired lines round his mouth and eyes, the set weariness of his lips, and without another word took the glass from him. It was three o'clock in the morning, and he must be exhausted, yet he was taking the trouble to attend to her hurts before going to his well-earned rest.

He waited in silence while she downed the fire-laden brandy which immediately sent soothing fingers deep inside her to still the pain from her ankle and peaceful lethargy through the rest of her. When Ben took up the bandage and bound the reduced swelling with firm confident hands, she watched the bent concentration of his head and eyes with sleepily grateful regard, vaguely surprised that she had to force her eyelids open when he finished attending to her leg with a grunt of satisfaction and came round to sit beside her.

'Feel better?' his voice came from a long way away.

'Mmm,' she murmured, her eyes focusing on the tired blur of his face. 'You should have been a doctor, Ben, or a vet.'

'A good rancher has to be both those things to a certain extent,' he said so close to her ear that her eyes flew open to find that his face was just inches away. 'You were very wrong, though, about something else, Abby.'

'Wrong? About what?'

She tried to concentrate on waiting for his answer, but the feel of his lips touching lightly along her cheek distracted her and brought her arms up to circle his neck, lowering the sheet far below her shoulders.

At last the words came, accompanied by the warmth of his breath against her mouth. 'That I didn't have to look at you. I do have to look at you, Abby my love, but——'

The rest of his words were lost as his lips came down gently on hers and moved with undemanding warmth over the sensitive fullness he found there, his hand light yet abrasive as it traced a course across her smooth skin from rounded upper arm to shoulder to firm rise of breast beneath transparently silky material. Abby, drowning in a sea of uncharted ecstasy, tightened her fingers in his hair, felt them grow taut in their effort to bend his head closer to hers, his lips to mould more passionately to the yearning need she sought to convey ... it came as a physical pain when he lifted his head against the pressure of her hands and stared frowningly down into her blue eyes darkened with emotion.

'For God's sake, Abby,' he swore unsteadily, 'let me initiate at least this between us!'

The deep fork between her eyes portrayed more clearly than any words her puzzled bewilderment as the navy of her eyes met the sharpened green of his.

'Ben, I ...' She wanted to tell him about the feelings he

stirred in her, the inarticulate longing that made her want to submit to a man for the first time in her life ... but the moment passed and then it was too late.

'Abby! And—*Ben*?'

Harry's scandalised tones came from the door, which Ben had left partly open on his return from the kitchen. The housekeeper's bulky figure, wrapped in a dark plaid robe, was outlined like an avenging angel's, and Abby's eyes half closed in swooning misery when Ben's fingers clamped tightly to her arms and lifted them from his neck as he stood up.

'Don't get excited, Harry,' she heard him say smoothly. 'Abby's almost asleep—I'll explain outside ...'

Whether he did or not, Abby was in no position to know. Her eyes drooped as his tall figure left the bed and joined Harry's in the doorway, and she knew nothing but blackness, a velvet blackness her will was powerless to overcome ...

'You should have called on me to see to your ankle,' Harry reiterated stubbornly the following morning as Abby made desultory stabs at the hearty breakfast she had been presented with in bed. 'Can you imagine how I felt, coming along here thinking you must be ill, and finding you with your arms wrapped round Ben Franklin? And in that nightie, too!'

'It wasn't Ben's fault,' Abby put in without force.

'I'm not saying it was,' Harry returned tartly from her stance beside the bed. 'But he's a man with two good eyes in his head, and they had plenty to look at with that hit-and-miss nightdress! What possessed you to put that on last night, Abby?'

'Because I'm sick and tired of being thought of as an undersized boy!' Abby snapped, the tremor in her voice bringing a soft look of understanding to Harry's eyes.

'Oh, I see.' The housekeeper said no more until she had picked up the clothes Abby had discarded the night before. 'Ben explained about the brandy—that you weren't yourself, what with that and the sprained ankle and all.'

'He said that? That it was because of the brandy that I—that I——'

'What else would it have been? I made it very clear to Ben that you're not in the habit of throwing yourself at men in your bedroom.'

'I did not throw myself at him!' Abby cried indignantly. 'He was just as ...' Her voice cut off abruptly when memory of the scene flashed into her mind and she heard again Ben's frustrated: 'For God's sake, Abby, let me initiate at least this between us!'

'Mm.' Harry shot her a look of supreme comprehension from the door. 'Well, you've no need to worry about it. Ben understands.'

'Oh, he does, does he?' Furiously, Abby lifted the tray from her knees and made a violent move with her legs, crying out in irritation when her injured ankle reminded her sharply of its presence.

'Calm yourself,' Harry told her firmly as she came back to replace the tray. 'Eat your breakfast and forget about last night. Ben's pretty sure we won't be hearing any more from Dave Corben—or Wally either!' Her eyes resumed their censorious look. 'What possessed you to go out there with only Ben for support? I'm surprised he allowed it.'

'He doesn't have the right to allow or not allow where I'm concerned!' snapped Abby. 'All I had to do was remind him that I'm the boss around here and that he's just an employee like any of the other men.'

Harry shook her grey head despairingly. 'And then you expect him to be loving just because you put on a see-through nightie! There's more to being attractively feminine than displaying a half naked body, you know, Abby. I think it was very lucky it was Ben you had in here, not most of the other men I know!'

Colour had flamed to peony redness on Abby's cheeks, but her eyes sparkled dangerously as they looked up into the housekeeper's severe expression.

'Stop treating me like a child, Harry! I'm plenty old enough to know how to handle men ... I knew Dave Corben wouldn't hurt me last night.'

'No?' Harry returned drily. 'What about those bruises on

your wrist? Wasn't it Dave who put them there? And you'd have ended up with a lot worse if it hadn't been for Ben.' She turned back to the door with an impatient movement. 'Eat your breakfast before it's stone cold. Then I suggest you get changed into the pyjamas I've laid out for you in the bathroom. Ben's coming to see you later.'

'I don't want to see him!' Abby called after the re-treating figure, but the only reply was a door firmly closed and silence in the room.

When Harry ushered Ben in an hour later, Abby was sit-ting up against her pillows, long-sleeved blue-flowered pyjamas buttoned to form a vee just below her throat. She looked away as Ben's amused eyes flickered over the pyjamas and heard rather than saw him bring over a high-backed chair to sit beside the bed. Harry, saying she would bring coffee for them, bustled out of the room.

'So,' he said softly, hitching the chair closer to the bed, 'you found some after all.'

Abby frowned at him. 'Found what?'

'Pyjamas. I seem to remember you telling me last night——'

'I—I'd forgotten I had these,' she inserted hastily, turn-ing her eyes away again from the angry bruise on his cheek bone. 'Harry found them.'

'Mm. Well, how's the ankle this morning? Harry tells me you're like a newly caged wildcat, so I guess it's bothering you.'

'Not as much as it did last night,' she admitted, adding pointedly: 'I—I wasn't myself last night.'

'I know that,' he said easily with an overtone of what might have been regret. 'Neither was I, or you'd maybe have had cause to fire me this morning.'

His assumption that she would have been powerless to do anything about his advances had he been in the mood to make them irked her and she lashed out:

'Don't be so all-fired conceited! I'd never have let you . . .' Her voice trailed away and her lashes curved down to ob-scure her eyes.

'No?' There was soft laughter in his voice when he went on: 'I'd have said it was the other way round, now I come to think of it—would *I* have let *you*?' His smile broadened when she gasped and grew crimson, groping impotently for syllables to express her rage, his next words making it no easier for her to find her tongue. 'Redheads really do have lousy tempers, don't they?'

'You should know!' she choked out at last, her eyes flashing pinpoints of fire at his own dark red hair brushed neatly to one side.

'Ah, but some of us learn to control the less attractive parts of our nature.'

'You've a long way to go yet, then!' she tossed back into his frankly smiling countenance where strong white teeth gleamed behind sensuously shaped lips.

'Maybe so,' he shrugged, and grew more sober when Harry at last came into the room with their coffee and cinnamon cake still warm from the oven. 'Mmm ...' he sniffed, sighing as he looked up at the housekeeper. 'If you weren't already spoken for, Harry, I'd carry you off to the nearest church and marry you on the basis of that smell alone!'

'Huh! It would take an even bigger man than you to carry me anywhere,' she retorted disparagingly, though the rosy flush on her cheeks showed that she was pleased. 'Anyway, when you do jump into the sea of matrimony, it'll be with somebody a lot younger and prettier than me.'

'Oh, I don't know, Harry,' Ben said thoughtfully, helping himself to a wedge of the cake. 'What's inside a woman is a lot more important than the outer layer—though it helps if she's easy on the eye too.'

'Talking about that—Verna just called to ask you to call for her half an hour or so later than arranged to bring her out here. Something about the store, she said.'

'Fine, thanks Harry,' he returned without batting an eyelid in Abby's direction.

'Have some cake, Abby?' Harry offered the plate.

'No.' Abby sent a malevolent look in the housekeeper's direction. 'What's Verna coming here for?'

'Because I asked her,' Ben inserted blandly. 'She's offered to cook dinner for me as a change from my own monotonous efforts.'

'Isn't that charitable of her?' Abby sneered, hardly notic-ing when Harry murmured something about getting on and went hastily from the room.

'I thought so,' Ben agreed comfortably. 'She has a nice nature.'

'Maybe you should ask her husband about her nature!' she retorted waspishly, and Ben's brows rose.

'I don't think that's necessary. I'm a pretty good judge of character.'

'I certainly hope so, for your own sake,' she warned darkly, her mouth compressed to firmness. 'As it happens, it might not be possible for you to see Verna tonight.'

'Oh? And why would that be?'

'Because I want you to take the men up to Mellon's field and start cutting. That has to be done before the cattle are moved up to summer pasture, and with Wally gone ...'

'We can get just as much accomplished with an early start tomorrow morning,' he said evenly, standing and re-placing his cup on the tray. 'By the time we could get up there now, the day would be half gone.'

'Nevertheless, I'm telling you to go up there today!' she repeated sharply.

'And I'm telling you that there's no way I'm going before tomorrow morning.' His face had paled under the tan, making the bruise on his cheek stand out more starkly, and she could see that the temper he had boasted of con-trolling was dangerously near the surface. 'You've hired me to do a job—for God's sake, let me do it my way.'

Abby pushed away a small stab of fear and mocked: 'Goodness, you've really taken Verna to heart, haven't you? You'll even risk your job for the chance of having a cosy evening with her!'

'That's more than a man could count on with you!' he threw back with brutal harshness as he went to the door with lean-hipped strides. His head swivelled round from there. 'As for the job, it's yours any time you want to ask for it.'

Her eyes blazed momentarily into the cold green of his, then her gaze faltered and dropped away. He had made that offer knowing that she had no choice but to keep him on. Without Dave—and now without Wally—she would be helpless, especially tied to bed as she was.

Ben said nothing more, contenting himself with a contemptuous shrug of his broad shoulders before they disappeared through the doorway, the door closing with a decisive snap behind him.

Abby threw herself back on the pillows, resenting the angry tears that scalded her eyes. What was happening to her? Since Ben Franklin's arrival at the ranch, the previously even tenor of her life had gone awry. He had stirred up emotions in her which she had barely known existed, emotions she was too inexperienced to handle. The boys she had known seemed just that compared to Ben's worldly man's way, a way that drew her dormant senses to life and made her crave the feel of his lips on hers, the touch of his male hands on her body, the urge to submit to his dominant force. Was this love? Her admiration and respect for his knowledge and skill in the ranching field, the only one she knew—was that love? The tearing hand of jealousy that gripped her insides when Verna was mentioned, and her own dishonest hint that Verna had hidden faults Ben knew nothing about—could that be love?

If all these things added up to love, she wanted none of them, precluding as they did the independence of thought and action that was as natural to her as breathing.

CHAPTER SIX

ABBY had hopped across the hall and into the big low-ceilinged room which had been her father's for as long as she could remember, past the wide bed he had slept in alone since her mother's death. The window there gave an unobstructed view of the gravelled forecourt, which her own did not, and she had been stationed there behind the thick mesh curtains for only a short while when Ben's dark green station wagon swung round from the drive and swished across the gravel to park at the far end closest to his bungalow.

Breath caught in her throat when Ben's long figure unfolded from the driver's side. Even from this distance she could see the freshly shaved smoothness of his chin, the brushed neatness of his hair, the bronze matching colour of his casual shirt, and well tailored brown slacks.

For a moment she thought Verna hadn't come after all, but then she realised that the dark girl was waiting for Ben to come round and open the door for her. Such simpering helpless femininity, Abby fumed scornfully, but a wistful expression crossed her blue eyes when she saw Ben hand an attractively dressed Verna from the car as if she was made of Dresden china. He had never opened the car door for her, Abby! The radiant smile Verna used to convey her thanks reached the courtyard to where Abby stood at the window, and must have shattered Ben because his head was bent for a long time over Verna's, an answering smile gleaming whitely in his bronzed face.

When he put a casual hand on the other girl's waist to ead her to his bungalow, Abby turned away and hopped back across the room, tears blinding her progress, though she could not have said whether they were of rage or sadness.

'Abby! What in the world are you doing out of bed?' Harry scolded, coming along the passage bearing a tray with Abby's dinner arranged on it.

'I—I just wanted to check on something in Dad's room.' Abby propelled herself in front of the housekeeper until she flopped on the bed and replaced the covers over her breathless body.

'You have to wait until now to check something in your father's room?' Harry settled the tray over Abby's knees and refrained from looking at her when she said casually: 'Verna looked very nice, didn't she? That oatmeal dress suits her colouring so well it could have been made specially for her.'

'It probably was!' Abby concurred resentfully, then her stricken eyes met the knowing wisdom of Harry's. 'I have a right to know who's coming and going at Cedar Hills,' she blustered to cover her embarrassment.

'Of course you have, dear,' Harry said comfortably. 'Especially the attractive women your foreman entertains in his bungalow.'

'I thought *she* was to be entertaining *him* with her cooking!'

'Yes, well ...' Harry sighed. 'Having been married, she knows how best to please a man.'

'Obviously she didn't please the one she married too well, did she?'

'We don't know that, do we? Verna's always struck me as a gentle creature, too good for that arty fellow she married.'

Abby frowned down into the breaded veal chops bordered with fluffy mashed potatoes and garden peas. 'Why did she marry him, then?'

'Love strikes in the most unlikely places,' Harry said with unusual poesy as she went to the door. 'Eat your supper now before it goes cold. I'll bring dessert as soon as Phil and I have had our first course.'

Love strikes in the most unlikely places indeed! Abby spent only a moment or two pondering this before succumbing to the healthy appetite which took over where her nose function ended. Veal cooked to tender perfection melted in her mouth, and it was only when her plate was almost clear that she gave a thought to the possibility of cooking such a meal herself. The art of cooking couldn't be all that hard to master if Verna was such an expert that she could offer her services to Ben.

What was she preparing at this moment? Agonising visions of a neatly aproned Verna laughing provocatively at Ben while she tossed off a mouthwatering meal with effortless skill crossed Abby's mind and left such a sour taste in her mouth that she pushed away the remainder of her dinner, even refusing the strawberry shortcake Harry brought along a few minutes later.

To her credit, Harry made no remark about the sudden loss of appetite, satisfying herself with a sweep of her eyes over the nearly empty plate that her young employer had had enough to keep body and soul together.

'Would you like Phil to bring the TV in?' she suggested. 'Or I have my latest book club selections, you might like them.'

'No ... no, thanks, Harry. I'll listen to the radio for a while and then I'm sure I'll go to sleep. Make up for last night.'

But sleep was elusive, and Abby clearly heard Ben's car departing just after ten, taking Verna back to town. Not a late evening, she mused pensively. Hardly enough time to wash the dishes after their meal and sit down for a while. Had they sat cosily together on the sofa near the fireplace? How long would it have taken for Ben to put his arms round the oatmeal dress, to find Verna's willing lips and make love to her with his own in a way Abby knew only too well? The pain in her ankle as she moved restlessly under the covers was as nothing to the pain grinding at her heart. Why did Ben Franklin have to come here in the first place? She had been happy before that—well, content if not happy, and Abby was just beginning to realise the value of contentment and peace of mind.

She started up from a half-formed dream when his car crunched over the gravel once more. The hands on the luminous dial of her bedside clock showed two-thirty ... more than enough time for a protracted love session. What in the world could they have been doing for four hours? Not wanting to think about the answer to that one, Abby fell suddenly and deeply asleep.

Ben left for Mellon's field the next morning without making an effort to see her, and Abby told herself it didn't matter. Ranch business must be conducted as normal, however emotionally torn its owner might be.

The quietness prevailing over the ranch with most of the men gone made Abby restless, and halfway through the morning she said when Harry brought her coffee: 'I'll go mad if I have to stay in this bed another minute! I'm getting up, even if it's just to sit in the living room.'

'Then I'll have Phil come and carry you in,' Harry told her firmly. 'Relax and drink your coffee while I find him.'

So it was that Debby found her in the living room with her foot propped on a stool when she called an hour later. The pink floral dress the dark girl was wearing brought out a glow in her olive-toned cheeks, a sparkle to her eye, and Abby looked at her with grudging admiration.

'How did you know I was nursing a sick ankle?' she asked curiously after the preliminary greetings were over.

'Verna told me, of course,' Debby returned lightly, pulling a tub chair closer to Abby's and sinking into it. 'Didn't you know she was out here last night?'

'Was she?' Abby asked disinterestedly. 'Oh, yes, I think I did hear something about a visitor ... she didn't come and see me.'

'Well ...' Debby began, then hesitated. 'Ben told her about you twisting your ankle in one of the pastures, and said you weren't in the mood for visitors.'

'He did, did he? I just wish that man would keep his nose out of my affairs!' Though one thing in his favour was that he evidently hadn't mentioned Dave and the cattle stealing to Verna.

'In a way, your affairs are his, though, aren't they?' Debby pointed out sensibly, eyeing her friend worriedly. 'Why don't you like him, Abby? I thing he's a positive dream, and Verna likes him a lot—if she sees much more of him, I can see she'll get over Darrel in no time at all.'

'What's there to get over?' asked Abby moodily. 'If she was so crazy about Darrel, why didn't she stay married to him?'

Debby was thoughtful. 'Sometimes you can love a person, but not be able to be with them—if you see what I mean,' she laughed with a faint aura of embarrassment.

'I gather from your bubbly mood that that isn't your problem with Al Smith! When's the happy day?'

Colour deepened in Debby's face until it was a brick red shade. 'That's one reason I came out to see you, apart from wanting to cheer you up. Al's asked me to marry him, Abby, and I've said yes.'

Abby's eyes were round blue orbs on her friend's. Her question had been more sarcastic than sincere, and her breath seemed knocked from her body for a few moments.

'You mean you're going to *marry* him?'

'Yes,' softly. 'Remember how we used to say we'd never fall in love and get married? But when the real thing comes along, you don't even think twice about it. It's as if you've found the other half of yourself, and you can't imagine your life without that other half.' Her eyes grew pensive as they went over Abby's frowning face. 'You'll know what I mean when the right one comes along for you. There just isn't any way to describe it.'

'Don't you feel sorry for me, Debby Warner! I won't be sitting knitting in the parlour waiting for Mr Right to happen by!' She glowered at her friend for a moment, then they both burst into helpless laughter.

'You can't even knit!' Debby giggled.

'Neither can you,' Abby pointed out, sobering again.

'But I'm willing to learn if Al would like to wear sweaters I've put together myself—there's all kinds of things I'm interested in all of a sudden. Mom nearly fainted the other night when I offered to make dinner completely on my own ... and Dad thought he'd be getting a duplicate of the meals Verna turns out when she has the time.'

'What's wrong with Verna's meals?'

'Oh, nothing, I guess, but they're not very substantial. I suppose it's because she was married to an artist—she goes in for pretty-looking but unfilling things, and Dad likes to feel he's done more than nibble round the edges without ever coming to the real thing.'

Abby was thoughtful as the conversation turned to less important subjects, and didn't feel particularly disappointed when Debby said she couldn't stay for lunch. When Harry came in with a tray of soup and sandwiches after her friend had gone, Abby said with seeming casualness:

'Men like hearty meals, don't they, Harry?'

The housekeeper shot a wondering glance at the downcast eyes. 'Not only men,' she reminded her. 'You can put away a healthy amount yourself—and I enjoy food.'

'I was thinking,' Abby went on as if she hadn't heard, 'I should learn to do a thing or two around the kitchen. What would happen if you had to go away or something? I'd *look* like scrambled eggs after three days!'

'They *could* become a little boring after that time,' Harry agreed drily, adding half disinterestedly: 'Why don't you make use of these few days when you can't get out? You can sit in the kitchen just as well as in here, and watch me.'

'I've been watching you off and on for years,' Abby snorted, 'and I still can't do more than scramble eggs and make toast.'

'But you've never been interested before. Incentive's a wonderful thing, and you learn a lot more if you put your mind to it.'

So it happened that Abby spent the several days of her confinement to the house close to the housekeeper in the kitchen, watching Harry's plump expert fingers turn out the mouthwatering meals Abby had always taken for granted. Familiar kitchen odours soothed her senses, and when she appeared to become restless, Harry gave her tasks to do at the kitchen table. She became absorbed in cookbooks, and took them to bed to ponder over, realising before too long that cooking was more a matter of common sense and practice than a gift direct from heaven bestowed only on a few.

Five days after Ben's departure for the hayfields, when Abby was able to bear her weight on the ankle for quite long periods, she herself cooked the dinner for Phil, Harry and herself, insisting that Harry leave the kitchen so that she wouldn't be tempted to interfere.

And when Abby took the juicy brown roast from the oven and set it before Phil for carving, the housekeeper and her husband were loud in their praises for her efforts which had produced a more than passable meal of browned potatoes, carrots and green beans besides the meat and rich gravy. Abby had insisted on laying the dining room table, and they were about to dine in state when a sharp knock sounded at the front door. It was Harry who jumped up to answer it, coming back into the room a few moments later with a lean and fit-looking Ben behind her.

'Look who's back!' she announced, pleased smiles wreathing her face.

Abby's hands began to tremble uncontrollably at her place at the head of the table, and she willed the hot colour flooding her cheeks to go back where it came from, but it remained to cast a sparkle into her eyes when Ben spoke.

'I'm sorry, I didn't realise you'd just be sitting down to eat. I came to let you know how the cutting went, but it'll keep till later.'

'Why don't you stay and eat with us, Ben?' Harry asked, lifting questioning eyes in Abby's direction. 'There's more than enough food here. Abby cooked enough for a couple of small armies.'

His brows rose even higher than Harry's as his eyes went over the colourfully laden table. '*Abby* cooked it?'

'Every bit of it herself,' Harry beamed proudly. 'Doesn't it look wonderful?'

'Smells even better,' he sniffed appreciatively. 'Will you mind if I join you?' he asked Abby directly, his eyes holding the memory of their last meeting.

'Of course not,' she shrugged. 'As Harry said, there's plenty here.' She indicated the chair beside Phil to her right and Ben dropped into it, helping himself immediately to vegetables the moment Harry put a large dinner plate and cutlery before him.

Abby began to fill her own plate, though her hunger had inexplicably vanished. But it wasn't inexplicable, she told herself. The trembling, the increased rhythm of her heart-beat, the joy flooding her veins all told her that she was more than glad to see him again. It was only now, when he sat near her in freshly donned light plaid shirt, his strong white teeth showing clearly against the deepened tan of his face as he answered a remark of Harry's, that Abby realised how much she had missed him.

'How *did* the cutting go?' she asked with forced casualness.

'Pretty well,' Ben nodded. 'The men are finishing off, and they should be back some time tomorrow. It's good quality hay.'

'I thought it would be,' Abby said eagerly, forgetting everything in favour of her first love, ranching. 'The weather was just right early in the season, and now with this warm sun to finish it off ...'

'Right,' he agreed, reaching for the thickly sliced beef Phil had cut from the roast and ladling dark brown gravy generously over it. 'With a second cut from that later on, and the overall output from the higher pastures you should have enough to keep you going over the winter.'

Abby's hands gripped tightly to the knife and fork in her hands, her eyes riveted to her plate. Ben couldn't have made it much plainer that when winter came, he himself would not be involved with Cedar Hills. Where would he be, then? Tormenting himself by being near his brother's wife? With the newly divorced Verna? If the last was the case, at least he wouldn't be enjoying a meal as he obviously was now if he had Verna's bits and pieces to contend with, she thought with unusual spitefulness, looking up guiltily when she realised he was addressing her.

'I'm sorry, I was thinking about—something else. What did you say?'

As if his green eyes had dipped into the recesses of her brain and laid bare her thoughts, he gave a sardonic smile and repeated: 'I just asked if your ankle was better, but that's a foolish question under the circumstances. You couldn't have cooked this meal if it wasn't.' Unspoken was his surprise that she had suddenly blossomed into a more than passable cook in his absence.

'And a delicious meal it is too, Abby,' Phil put in, resting to make room for more. 'You'll make a good wife for some lucky man.'

'Being a wife isn't one of my ambitions,' Abby returned sharply, upset by the turn her thoughts had taken before Ben interrupted them.

Harry, unperturbed, chuckled and said: 'That's what most people say, honey, till the right one comes along. Look at Debby, she can't wait to marry Al Smith and she was pretty much like you.'

'Well, I just hope her marriage is more successful than her sister's!' Abby choked out, rising and muttering something about dessert as she went with a slight limp to the door.

She had cut the peach upside-down cake into wedges and filled a glass bowl with whipped cream when she looked up and saw Ben's lazily long figure propped against the doorframe, his eyes watching her with a faintly commiserating look.

'Does the thought of your friend's marriage upset you that much?' he asked softly, and when she made no reply, busying herself instead with plugging in the percolator, continued as he came across to the table: 'I wonder why you have such a thing about men and marriage, Abby? You're a pretty girl, and could be beautiful if you'd put aside those bristles now and then.'

'That's all men think about, isn't it?' she flared, spinning round to face him. 'They're so idiotic they can't see under all the gook on dressed-up dolls and then they complain when it's too late that she wasn't what she seemed.' Tears that were only partly temper trembled on the brink of her eyes and sent a tremor to the soft fullness of her lips, and she bent to pick up the tray, blinking rapidly.

Ben's hands grasped further along the laden tray and set it down again before coming up to her shoulders, turning her round and drawing her to him gently, one hand cupping her chin and lifting it to the green inspection of his eyes. Eyes that were no longer mocking, or sardonic, or hard, but Abby couldn't have found a word to describe them at that moment.

'The man who gets you will never have cause to complain on that score, Abby . . . he'll know exactly what he's getting. And he'll know, too, that there's only one way to tame a little hellion like you!'

The warm dryness of his lips covered the stinging reply on hers and left her gasping inwardly. His hand left her chin to cradle her throat, the other moving soothingly across her back in the same way he would gentle a fractious horse . . . but there was nothing gentle about the dominating force thrusting against her mouth and demanding, in a wordless battle, her yielding and response . . . a response she fought against with the clenched balls of her fists against the ungiving surface of his chest, the side-to-side movement of her head that only served to increase the pressure of his kiss . . .

His hands came up to hers and forced her fingers open, clamping them to the swift beat of his heart before lifting them to his neck, leaving them there and gathering her closer to the damp heat of his body. Her hands rose to his hair with the intention of using it as a lever to pull his head away, but the power of decision seemed to leave her suddenly when she felt the cool thickness between fingers that unexpectedly flexed, then pressed against his head to bring it closer. Submission was there in the softly pliant curve of her body to the unyielding demand of his, the warm sweetness of her lips that opened like a flower under the lessening abrasion of his forceful mouth, the long-drawn sigh that was drawn from her when at last his lips moved to kiss quickly along her jaw until his face was buried in the tender softness of her neck. His voice came from there, muffled and unsteady.

'Whoever he is . . . he might die in the attempt . . . but he'll think it was worth it . . .'

Whoever he is! If Ben had written the words in block letters on a placard he couldn't have made it more clear that the man he referred to was not himself. Did he think she would submit that readily to any male who chanced to force his attentions on her? That all a man had to do to win a woman was to exert his superior physical strength?

Sensing her withdrawal in the stiffening of her body,

Ben raised his head and stood away from her, though his hands still lay loosely on her waist. 'Now what?' he questioned, lifting his brows in a thick arc as he surveyed her quizzically. 'You were fine until I said——' He broke off abruptly, and his eyes lost the languid warmth the love-making had brought to them. At last he said quietly: 'That man can't be me, Abby, unless ...'

Unless he tidied away one or two matters like Verna and his sister-in-law, Sylvia, either of whom appealed to him far more than Abby Mackenzie! Hurt pride made Abby's voice stiffly sarcastic.

'You're even more egotistical than most men, Ben Franklin! If I was on the lookout for a man—which I'm not!—you'd be the last one I'd choose. If and when I do marry, it won't be to somebody who's still in the Dark Ages as far as equality goes. Why don't you try your cave-man tactics on Verna from now on? She'd love them!'

'I will—and she does,' he retorted frostily, turning to pick up the dessert tray with white-knuckled hands and checking his long stride at the door to look back at her pityingly. 'I doubt if you'll ever learn what women like Verna know by instinct—that there can never be real equality between a man and a woman in the way you mean. There are always times when one gives more than the other, but it evens itself out in time.'

'Thanks for the mini lecture,' she jeered, her eyes flickering stonily over his set face where a muscle twitched at his jaw, but her hands trembled when he had gone and she turned away to unplug the percolator. The knowledge that he was right did nothing to dispel the sharp-edged barbs of pain knifing through her which made her breath come in short gasps.

Ben's confirmation of her own wild imaginings of a passion filled evening with Verna—an evening that had stretched to the small hours of the morning—filled her with a stark despair she had never experienced before. And, struggling with another thought that pushed into her mind, she followed him to the dining room where the dessert dishes had already been set out. Her independent spirit had been in danger of being swamped by the first man to reach behind the closely woven surface she presented to the world, stirring the slumbering sensuous part of her nature.

But it wouldn't happen again, she vowed, taking her place at the table and ignoring Harry's searching look at her flushed face and tousled hair. Ben Franklin could make love to all the Vernas in the world, but it wouldn't affect Abby one bit ... she'd make very sure of that.

Days passed, and Abby's thoughts were filled more with her horse, Glory, than with Ben. The mare was restless as her confinement approached, relaxing only when Abby devoted her full attention to her. Even the exercise period Abby insisted on each day in the paddock adjoining the barn where Glory awaited the birth was whittled down until the mare showed reluctance to leave the loose box at all.

'How is she?' Ben's laconic drawl came from the half open double doors to the barn one day about a week after their confrontation in the kitchen. Abby had been quite successful at avoiding his tall lean-hipped figure except for the necessary meeting on ranch business which he had seemed as anxious to terminate as she was. On two occasions, she had heard him drive off before supper, schooling herself not to listen for his return but knowing each time that he came back well before eleven.

'She'll do,' Abby shrugged, leaving the horse to come across to the door, her eyes beginning to spark dangerously when Ben passed her nonchalantly and went to the mare, running expert hands over her side and murmuring soothingly to her pricked up ears. 'I told you she's all right!'

'I know you did,' quietly, 'but I wanted to see for myself. I've helped quite a few mares foal over the years.' With a last pat, he rejoined Abby and looked levelly at her flashing eyes.

'Well, this is one time when Glory and I can do without your masculine expertise!' she snapped, thumbs hooked belligerently into the waistband of her tightly fitting jeans.

His casual shrug infuriated her further. 'Glad to hear it. I'm expecting a visitor tonight, and I wouldn't want to be disturbed.' Giving an ironic flip of his fingers to his offwhite brimmed hat, he strode away leaving Abby gazing after him in impotent rage. If she wanted help with Glory, he'd be the last one she'd call—even young Joe would be preferable!

But even as she thought of the young hand, a station wagon swept round from the direction of the bunkhouse and the entire complement of single Cedar Hills employees left for their usual Friday night in town, not to return until the early hours of next morning if previous experience was anything to go by. The married men lived away from the ranch area, except for Phil.

Abby brightened at the thought of Phil. If she needed help, he would be the ideal one to give it. A gleam of triumph lit her eyes as she made her way past Ben's bungalow to the main house and heard his cheerful whistle above the hissing rush of the shower that came from the half open bathroom window. She almost wished Glory would foal that night in order to show him how little he was needed in her life.

Harry's blanched face met her in the hall, the housekeeper more agitated than Abby had ever seen her.

'Oh, Abby, I was just coming out to find you!'

'What in the world is wrong?' Abby asked, her hand going out automatically in a gesture of comfort to the older woman who had always been the rock of steadiness in her own life.

'It's Jim—our Jimmy's been hurt in a road accident. Ellen, his wife, just called and asked us to go down there right away. He's—in hospital at Kamloops.'

'Oh, Harry! I'm so sorry. Is it—is he very badly hurt?'

The housekeeper's face crumpled. 'Ellen wouldn't say, but it must be bad if she's asking us to go down there in such a hurry.' She wrung her hands. 'And what about you, Abby? I hate to go off and leave you on your own like this.'

'Don't be silly, Harry. I'll be just fine—I've managed before when you've been away on holiday.'

'But I've always left things you could heat up for meals,' Harry said worriedly. 'There's nothing prepared in the freezer.'

'I'll manage,' Abby said firmly. 'I'll enjoy trying out some of those recipes I boned up on when my ankle was sprained.'

She hugged the plump figure fiercely for a moment before pushing her gently away. 'Go and get your things packed— does Phil know?'

'Yes, he's packing what he needs now.'

'Then he'll want to get away as soon as possible, so get your things and *go*, Harry.'

It was half an hour later when the elderly couple set off in their old but serviceable car, Abby waving them off after telling them to be sure and let her know about their son's condition as soon as possible. Phil, with his quiet placid temperament, would see that they arrived safely.

Heaving a huge sigh when the car was no longer visible, Abby turned back into the house and, ignoring Harry's explicit instructions regarding the dinner already cooking on the stove, turned off the heat and made herself a sandwich instead. Hunger was the last thing she felt at that moment, and the cooked food could be warmed up for the next night's supper.

Carrying a tray with the sandwich and a tall glass of milk into the living room, Abby sat in a chair close to the window where she had an unbroken view of the peacefully green pastures stretching to the road quarter of a mile away. Always it had been this view that brought her comfort when needed, especially this evening when the well laid out and carefully tended flower garden at the rear of the house would remind her of Phil. There was a big enough lump in her throat already.

Lost in thought, she failed to see the small white car coming along the drive until it turned into the forecourt and went to park at the far end close to Ben's. Verna. So anxious to come to Ben that she had driven herself out from town. Abby looked disinterestedly on as the dark girl, dressed tonight in sleeveless linen dress of pale coral, took numerous small bags from the back of the car and turned towards Ben's bungalow. Another gourmet meal, Abby thought with subdued vindictiveness. Well, at least he'd be pleased that it was prepared with whitely feminine fingers!

Concern for Glory drove her out of the house again an hour or so later, and her eyes were drawn through the screen door Ben had re-hung when the weather grew warmer. Verna's softly husky laughter floated out to her, and she saw the cosy twosome installed at the small dining table close to the kitchen, their meal obviously almost ended but their heads close together over flickering candlelight.

Candles! she thought disgustedly, her small booted feet almost stamping their way across to the barn. Verna had always been inclined towards flights of romantic fancy, even to insisting on a candlelit wedding ceremony with all the trimmings when she married the man she was now divorcing. How could Ben——

All thoughts of the cosily dining couple vanished when Abby entered the barn and heard Glory's low whinnies of distress. The liquid dark eyes turned trustingly to her when she ran across and laid a hand on the damp warmth of the mare's neck and whispered:

'Oh, darling, it's time, isn't it? Soon all the waiting's going to be over.'

Her arms circled the shifting horse's neck and her face touched the velvet sleekness of Glory's, murmuring soothing endearments into her ear. That something might go wrong with the birth never entered her head in any serious way. Giving birth on a ranch was the most natural thing in the world, and if there had been problems, her father had never mentioned them when presenting his daughter with a new colt or calf which had already been born and cleaned by the mother before Abby was brought on the scene.

It was only after time had slipped by without any appreciable difference in Glory's distress—except perhaps an added sense of frustrated agony conveyed from the mare to herself—that doubt entered her mind. Surely it didn't take this long for a mare to foal in the normal way?

Her own exhaustion was almost as great as Glory's when she brought over a stool and sat back against the slatted wood enclosing the loose box. The frequent rub-downs she had given Glory no longer seemed to bring comfort, and she closed her eyes against the hypnotic appeal in the mare's eyes for her to do something to relieve her.

The truth was, she admitted at last, that she hadn't any idea of how to relieve the straining animal. She should have called for help as soon as she had seen Glory's condition, but her own confidence in being able to cope with a natural happening had proved over-inflated. Now Glory was suffering because of her stupidity ... her beloved horse could even die because of it. Starting up with a sob, she rushed to the door and ran right into the man she had intended to seek.

'Abby? I saw the lights—is it Glory?'

Ben's hands had fastened on her upper arms with a firmness she welcomed at that moment, and she forgot her previous scathing rejection of his help.

'Yes,' she gasped, looking up at him appealingly, 'but there's something wrong. Please, Ben, will you help her?'

His eyes narrowed as they went to the exhausted horse, taking in the dejected droop of her head, the hopeless stillness of her body, then he thrust Abby away from him and strode quickly over to the box.

'How long has this been going on?' he whipped out, his hands feeling the side and underparts of the horse.

'I—I don't know what time it is,' Abby stammered. 'I don't have my watch on. But I think she'd just started when I came back around eight o'clock——'

'Eight?' he repeated, turning to look incredulously at Abby and swearing under his breath. 'It's almost midnight—why didn't you get help?'

Quickly she explained the absence of everyone who might have aided, adding in a faltering voice: 'You—you said you didn't want to be disturbed, and—I thought I could manage by myself,' she ended miserably, expecting and receiving the withering hardness in his green eyes.

'You damned little fool! You could lose this horse because of your stubbornness!' His fingers went to the buttons on his pale yellow shirt. 'Get me some hot soapy water—now!' he roared in exasperation when he hesitated dazedly, her eyes dark blue pools of distress as they went from him to the unnatural stillness of the horse.

Then without a word she went quickly to get what he had ordered, her only conscious thought one of grateful thanks that the problem had been taken off her shoulders. Ben was now in charge of Glory's destiny, instinct that had no time for second thoughts telling her that if anyone could save the mare, he could. She herself could only be the willing tool for his commands.

When she came back with the water, Ben was stripped to the waist and she watched numbly as he plunged one arm into the steamy hotness of the bucket. 'Wh-what are you going to do?' she asked nervously.

'I'm going to have to go in there and see what's holding things up,' he replied tersely, not raising his head from the crouching position he had taken to splash the soaped water on his arm as far as his shoulder.

'Oh.' Abby's voice came out in a helpless sigh and his eyes swept up and over the sickly paleness in her face. He stood up, water dripping from his arm.

'Go and hold her head and talk to her while I do this,' he said gruffly, waiting until she had complied before stepping resolutely to the horse.

CHAPTER SEVEN

'OH, Ben, he's beautiful!' Abby breathed only minutes later when Ben carried the leggy colt round to his mother's front and laid him within easy licking distance of the maternal tongue. Abby's eyes shone as she looked up into his sweat streaked face. 'How did you do it?'

His hair had fallen over his brow in damp strands, and his wide chest lifted and fell with heavy breaths when he said: 'The little one had got tangled up in there ... all I did was turn him round a bit. The rest he and Glory did between them.'

Abby's eyes filled with tears as they took in the contentedly licking Glory and her fragile offspring. 'They could—both have died. Thank you, Ben.'

For a long moment his eyes held to hers, then he shrugged slightly and went back to the cooled water, sluicing both arms and running wet hands over his chest. Abby set her numb legs into motion to get him a towel, and he took it from her with a nod of thanks.

'Why didn't you get Phil to help you if the other men were away?' he asked almost casually as he rubbed himself dry with vigorous strokes. 'Even though I was—otherwise engaged, you could have asked him.'

'I—I couldn't,' she faltered, and told him about the accident to Phil and Harry's son. Tears drawn from her exhausted spirit spilled from her eyes and ran down her cheeks, and she felt herself being drawn gently against the dampness of his chest, his arms closing round her to hold her with such incredible tenderness that the tears flowed with even greater force, wetting her cheeks and the dark red hairs covering Ben's heart beating with steady rhythm against her ear.

For a long time she stayed in the heavenly shelter of those protective arms, until at last Ben raised her head and dabbed the wetness from her cheeks with the towel he still held in one hand. His eyes dropped then to the trembling curve of her mouth, and she knew that if he kissed her at that moment, all her weakened defences would come tumbling down. How much she had wanted him to kiss her was evident in the tug of disappointment she felt when he pushed her away slightly and said:

'Hungry? Did you eat supper?'

'I—I had a sandwich,' she admitted. 'I wasn't very hungry after Harry and Phil left.' The sudden surge of appetite must have shown in her face, because he squeezed her and smiled faintly.

'Let's go and cook ourselves something substantial. Glory doesn't want us around any more, anyway.'

While he reached for his shirt and shrugged his shoulders into it, Abby gazed at the supremely contented mare and her foal, obviously oblivious of their presence.

'There's a perfectly good meal at the house,' she offered, strangely shy when Ben came to join her and walk with her to the door. 'Harry cooked it before she left. Pork chops and baked beans and——'

'That sounds wonderful,' he said with such heartfelt anticipation that she looked curiously at him.

'How can you be hungry again? You've just eaten with Verna.'

Out in the open his eyes were obscured in the moonlight glimmering from the sky behind his head. 'Yes ... well,' he said heavily at last, putting a hand under her elbow to guide her to the main house, 'that was some time ago and I seem to be hungry again. Harry's pork chops sound just the thing to hit the spot.'

Abby said no more then, but did little to push away the exultant knowledge that in one respect at least Verna wasn't the answer to a rancher's prayer.

'Abby! Hi!'

Debby rushed from her sister's dress shop three days later when Abby paused briefly to look at the creations in the window. Dressed in a sober dark grey dress with boat neckline outlined in white, Debby's normally exuberant spirits seemed dampened to demure flatness.

'Why don't you come in and buy something?' she asked, a hint of her old grin appearing at the back of her eyes as they went over Abby's neat but unchic blue slacks and matching floral shirt.

'Not if I'd look like that in it!' Abby returned with blunt honesty. 'You remind me of Miss Smithers in first grade!'

Unabashed, Debby giggled. 'Don't be an idiot! I'm wearing this because I'm in charge of the store while Verna's away in Vancouver seeing about her divorce. Why don't you come in and try some things on for fun?'

'I don't think your sister would appreciate having her beautiful creations mauled about by non-buyers,' Abby retorted. 'Besides, I'm really not interested in pretty-pretty clothes.'

'Maybe not, but the men really go for them.' Debby linked her arm in her friend's and drew her resisting figure into the store with her. 'Even Fay Gorman's husband has a new light in his eye since Fay's been buying her clothes here.'

'You're putting me on!' Against her will, Abby smiled at the thought of the plump Fay Gorman re-attracting the attention of a husband who had long since stopped admiring his wife in favour of younger, slimmer girls.

'No, really. She actually came in and thanked Verna for saving her marriage!'

While she was speaking, Debby had drawn Abby further into the shop which, though small, was laid out in attractive displays and racks of clothing for any occasion from tennis to the most formal bridal ensemble.

'It must be—strange for Verna to hear that she's saving someone else's marriage while her own is going down the drain.'

'Oh, I don't think that side of it bothers Verna one bit. She's far from giving up her romantic ideas about marriage, you know. My guess is that it won't be too long before she's back in harness again.'

'You think so?' Abby murmured, lapsing into a thoughtful state when her friend pushed her into a cubicle at the rear of the store and went to attend to a customer at the other end after promising to come back with some dreamy things for Abby to try on.

Did Verna really contemplate marriage again so soon after the break-up of her first? Would it work out any better with Ben than it had with Darrel? Only if she learned to cook plainer fare than she had served up so far to Ben, Abby told herself with chalky asperity, then remembered her own lack of skill in culinary accomplishments. Still, he had enjoyed the roast dinner she had prepared without knowing he was coming, and his appreciation of Harry's pork chops the other night had been more than evident in the way he had pushed back his chair with a heartfelt sigh of satisfaction.

'There's a lot of truth in that old saying that the way to a man's heart is through his stomach, Abby,' he had pronounced, lighting up one of his thin cigars and drawing deeply on it while Abby poured coffee into their cups. 'Any woman who cooks like that deserves a man's heart and soul.'

'Harry has Phil's heart and soul already,' she had responded tartly, 'so I doubt if she'd be interested in yours.'

An odd look, almost of disappointment, had come into his eyes then. 'I'd forgotten you didn't cook it yourself,' he said quietly. 'It was almost as good as the meal you made once before.'

Now, as then, Abby's brows drew down in a frown. From those words, she might have thought Ben's heart and soul were hers ... yet he had done no more than kiss her forehead lightly when he left not long after, and had been no more than courteously polite when they met during the following two days. Had he and Verna come to some kind of an agreement that night of the colt's birth, an agreement that hinged on the successful outcome of Verna's divorce? It had been almost midnight when Verna left, plenty of time to come to a hundred such agreements.

Restless suddenly, Abby got to her feet from the corner stool and peeped through the curtains to where Debby was showing a petite middle-aged woman to the door. Wandering out of the cubicle, Abby looked with little interest over the display rack of evening wear situated at that end of the store, lighting on and fastening to a wax model wearing a flimsy concoction of electric blue which revealed more of the sepia-coloured plastic flesh than it concealed.

'Isn't it gorgeous?' Debby's voice came from behind her. 'Want to try it on?'

'Heavens, no!' Abby stepped backwards shaking her head. 'Can you see me in something like that?'

Debby regarded her thoughtfully. 'Actually I can ... that colour would do wonders for your eyes, though I can't imagine what the neckline would do to any man who would see you in it! Come on, Abby, try it on just for fun.'

The other girl was already undressing the model, which seemed to Abby to be staring disdainfully down at her own slacks-clad figure as if doubting her ability to wear anything so sheerly woven from dreams.

'All right, I will,' she said half defiantly, more to the model than Debby, and followed her friend to the cubicle, ushering her out with the words: 'I'll call you when it's time for the peep-show!'

And peep-show was just what it would be, she decided a few minutes later when the dress lay in filmy folds over her hips but touched very lightly on her breasts, leaving a remarkable amount of white flesh showing before the blue material caught at the outer edges of her shoulders and cascaded in wispy layers down her arms.

'I think the designer got his areas mixed up,' she called to Debby. 'He or she put the covering in the wrong place!'

Debby's jaw dropped open and her eyes became saucers when Abby drew the curtain back, prepared to laugh with her friend. 'Gosh, Abby, you look—great! Wow!—I hope Al never sees you in that, or I'll lose him for sure.'

'Oh, come on, Debby,' Abby sighed with a hint of impatience. 'You'd never in a million years find me wearing something like this. If I didn't expire of cold, I'd die of embarrassment!'

'Abby, you've got to wear it,' the other girl insisted. 'You'd never ever find another dress that does so much for you.'

'Your sister's made a pretty good saleswoman out of you,' remarked Abby drily, reminding herself of Verna and turning to survey herself in the three-way mirror again. 'Besides, where would I wear it?' she added with a trace of wistfulness.

'Have a party!' Debby enthused. 'It's been years since you had one at Cedar Hills.'

'Oh, I couldn't—not with Harry being away.'

'But you told me yesterday on the phone that her son's going to be okay—Harry wouldn't mind a bit, I know.'

'But ...' Abby bit her lip, then looked again at the dress which made her skin whiter, her eyes a deeper, more vivid blue.

'Come on, Abby, I'll help you with the eats—Mom will too, she loves preparing the food more than the party itself. And we can bring over our stereo and records.'

'But there's no reason for me to have a party,' Abby protested uselessly, for Debby immediately thought of a reason.

'You can have a christening party for the new colt! Nobody cares *why* you have a celebration, Abby,' her friend pointed out with weary logic, 'as long as you have one.'

In the end, Abby was persuaded that a party had been her own suggestion, and small fingers of anticipation crept up her spine as she went around town doing the rest of her shopping after signing a cheque larger than any she had ever paid out for a dress before. What would Ben think of it? At least with an outfit like that, he couldn't accuse her of being unfeminine!

Harry phoned again at the middle of the week, telling Abby that although her son was recovering more rapidly than expected, she and Phil would like to stay on with their daughter-in-law for a few more days.

'Are you managing all right, Abby?' she asked, anxiety evident in her voice over the miles.

'I'm fine,' Abby assured her, deciding to say nothing about the party on Saturday evening or the housekeeper would have insisted on coming back to cater for it. 'Stay down there as long as you want to, Harry, I'm sure Ellen needs you right now much more than I do—though I miss you,' she added with contrite haste.

'How's Ben?'

'Ben? He's fine too—he sends you his heart and soul.'

'His what?'

'His heart and soul—he shared the meal you left last Friday, and said a woman who cooks like that deserves his heart and soul.'

Harry chuckled. 'Tell him I'd know what to do with them if I was forty years younger!' She went on to ask about the new colt, and when Abby had filled her in on the details, said: 'What are you going to call him?'

There was a perceptible pause at Abby's end, then she said slowly: 'I think I'll name him Frank—how does that sound?'

An even longer silence ensued before Harry returned: 'I think it's just the right name for him, honey. Phil and I can't wait to see him—we should be back next Monday.'

After telling the housekeeper not to hurry on her account, Abby hung up and frowned thoughtfully. The decision to name the colt had come to her in a flash ... or perhaps it had been there in her subconscious waiting to pop out at the first opportunity. Would Ben appreciate the colt he had helped bring into the world being named after him? Whether he did or not, she sighed as she rose, it was the only way she could think of to acknowledge his skill in saving both Glory and her baby.

After his initial surprise at hearing of her plans for a party, Ben had been interestedly helpful, offering to string lights through the trees surrounding the garden patio at the rear of the house, and to see to the supply of drinks. The only discordant note between them came when he said with a sardonic lift of his eyebrows:

'I presume it's a "come as you are" party?'

'No, it isn't,' she retorted coolly. 'As it happens, I've bought a dress from your girl-friend's store.'

'Have you? Don't I feel the world shaking? You in a dress will be something to see,' he said, laughter in his voice, but Abby noticed that he made no effort to contradict that Verna was his girl-friend.

'You can bring Verna as your partner,' she tested with assumed casualness, watching his reaction from the corner of her eye, but his expression remained bland.

'Thank you. I'd have thought she would be coming anyway as her mother and sister are helping with the catering bit.'

'Yes—well, Verna's the kind who needs a man to escort her.'

'And you don't?'

'Of course not,' she returned indignantly. 'I'd hardly need an escort to my own party, and anyway, I don't need a man for any——' She broke off, reddening as her eyes met his and she remembered the night of the foal's birth and how much she had needed Ben then.

Fortunately Gary, the second youngest to Joe on the ranch, called to Ben for help at that moment, but Ben's sardonic smile stayed with Abby long after she had settled herself in the office. Why was it so difficult for her to remember that without Ben's help she would have lost the horse she loved so much ... without his protection the outcome of Dave Corben's midnight raiding party could have been far more serious? Why couldn't she be more like Verna, clingingly female and unashamed of her dependence on men? Ever since she could remember, Abby had had a driving need to prove herself the equal of men, not their inferior in any way—so why did Ben Franklin have the effect on her of wanting to melt into his arms and leave the harder facets of life to him?

Abby was about to leave the office late on Friday afternoon when the telephone rang. Throwing herself back into the chair behind the desk, she lifted the receiver and heard Debby's voice at the other end.

'Abby? I'm calling you for two reasons—one, how would you like to have me come and stay overnight with you and help you organise things for tomorrow?'

'I'd love it,' Abby returned enthusiastically. Although her own company was bearable most of the time, the absence of Harry and Phil in the house was beginning to make it feel less like home than a house Abby happened to spend a few hours in each night. 'There's not much left to do, but I'd be glad of some company.'

'Oh, come on, Abby,' her friend teased. 'You've got that gorgeous hunk of man by the name of Ben Franklin right there, and you're telling me you're *lonely*?'

'He's not the kind a girl asks in for a quiet game of cards,' Abby responded drily. 'Besides, we can't be together for two minutes without arguing about something or other.'

'Didn't you know that's supposed to be a good sign? It shows there's a chemical reaction between you.'

'Hm. The kind of chemical reaction we have is one that ends in fireworks and explosions! Anyway,' Abby steered the conversation away from the dangerous subject of Ben, 'what was the second thing you were calling about?'

'Oh, I almost forgot. Actually, it's to do with Ben as well. Verna got back from Vancouver today, and she wants to come out and see Ben tonight. Would you mind telling him that she'll bring stuff for dinner as usual?'

'What if he's planning on going out?' Abby queried waspishly.

'He's not,' Debby replied airily. 'They arranged that she'd see him as soon as she got back ... she just wasn't sure when that would be.'

'I suppose she wants to tell him that her divorce is final now,' probed Abby, surprising even herself by her curiosity.

'Could be. She hasn't mentioned it to any of us, so maybe she wants Ben to be the first to know.'

After arranging that Debby would come with her sister later, Abby put the phone down and sat quite still in the chair for several minutes before getting up woodenly to deliver the message to Ben. No wonder he had been treating her like a Dutch uncle lately ... he had been looking forward to receiving the news Verna was about to bring to him, that she was a free woman again. A woman intent on relinquishing that freedom as quickly as possible.

The open door to the bungalow signified that Ben was back, but there was no sign of him in the living room or kitchen when she peered through the fine mesh screen. Was there to be a repeat of their first encounter in the small house? Her hand gave a peremptory knock on the wood edge of the screen, and this time she remained outside until, a moment later, Ben's tall figure came from the bedroom area. Breathing a sigh of relief that his undressing had gone no further than the unbuttoning of his shirt, she said through the mesh:

'I have a message.'

'A message for me?'

She couldn't be sure because of the shadowing screen, but it seemed the wariness she had noted in his expression several times before crossed his face. Whatever it was, it had gone by the time he pushed the door outwards and asked her inside.

'Obviously it's for you or I wouldn't be here,' she said, irritably aware of the all-male force emanating from his hair-covered chest. 'Verna wants you to know that she's coming out tonight to make your dinner—as usual, the message said,' she added in a spirit of spitefulness, and was rewarded by a faint wince passing over his features.

'Thanks—for bringing the message. Er—Abby?' he called after her as she went back to the door. 'Do you like— pickled walnuts?'

'Pickled—*what*?' she swung round, expecting to see a superior smile on his mouth, but instead he looked more diffident than she had ever seen him.

'Walnuts ... they're a rare delicacy. Would you like to try some?'

'Not particularly, thanks.' She looked at him curiously. 'Why did you buy them if you don't like them?'

'I—um—didn't buy them, they were given to me.'

Understanding cleared her brow. 'Oh. Verna.'

'Yes, and I wouldn't want to offend her by having the whole jar left when she comes.'

Amazed, Abby stared at him. 'Ben Franklin, you're a coward!'

'I know,' he admitted humbly. 'Will you at least take the jar and hide it somewhere in the house? I'll think of a way of getting rid of it later.'

'Oh, all right, give it to me. Who knows, maybe Harry likes them.'

In a moment he was back with the fancily cut jar and handed it to her, leaning further forward to give her another of those light kisses on her forehead.

'Thanks, Abby.'

Pushing away the feeling of childish disappointment that he had treated her as a brother might by pecking her on the brow placatingly, Abby made her way back to the house and began to prepare the supper she and Debby would share. Following a recipe in one of Harry's cookbooks, she made beef slices in onion sauce on top of the stove, and was gratified two hours later when Debby exclaimed:

'Where did you learn to cook like this all of a sudden? You must be in love.'

'Why do I have to be in love to follow a perfectly straightforward recipe in a cookbook?' Abby demanded, chagrined, but her colour deepened nonetheless and her friend noted it.

'You *are* in love, admit it! Who is it, Abby?'

'Oh, don't be an idiot! Just because you——'

'I know!' Debby cried triumphantly. 'It must be Ben Franklin!' She sat up in her chair excitedly. 'He's the only new man around here, and you'd have to be made of stone not to notice those mile-wide shoulders and ice green eyes that send shivers up a girl's spine!'

'It sounds as if you're more in love with him than I am!' Abby remarked drily. 'You and your sister Verna seem to find him irresistable.'

Debby's brow wrinkled thoughtfully. 'I don't know about Verna. She says he's the most understanding man she's ever met, and she sees quite a lot of him, but——' she shrugged, 'I think myself she's still crazy about Darrel deep down.'

'Then why is she divorcing him? That's crazy!'

'Oh, I don't know. Al and I disagree sometimes, and it's frightening how quickly a little spat can balloon into something unmanageable. Mostly it's because one of us isn't willing to see the other's side. That could have happened to Verna and Darrel.'

'Well, I wouldn't say she's exactly pining her heart out

for him!' Abby said tartly as she rose and picked up the dishes.

That Verna wasn't pining at all was only too obvious the next evening when she came into the main house on Ben's arm, her dark eyes shiningly radiant as they looked up into his. The coffee-coloured dress she wore was a perfect foil for the black hair cascading over bare shoulders, and was only a shade darker than her skin.

Ben's eyes still held a smile when he looked up from Verna's animated face and saw Abby framed against the dark panelling at the back of the hall. The smile seemed to freeze on his face as his eyes went over the figure-hugging blue dress, then back to the expanse of marble-white skin exposed above it, finally rising to take in the red-gold cloud of softly brushed hair.

'My God, Abby, is it you?' he murmured when she came across to greet them. She liked the feel of gossamer round her legs as she walked, and she was glad, suddenly, that she had let Debby apply the make-up that deepened her eyes to the dark brilliance of sapphire, her lashes to a thick misty curtain over them, her lips to a translucent pale orchid.

'So you're the one who bought that dress,' Verna laughed, her voice attractively low. 'Debby wouldn't tell me, but I should have guessed, remembering the eternal secrets you two have been sharing since you were infants.' She looked up into Ben's face, where a frown had replaced the smile. 'Don't you just love that dress on Abby, Ben?'

'What there is of it,' he nodded brusquely, his eyes staring hard at the clear white flesh swelling up from the bodice.

'Oh, don't be so old-fashioned, sweetie,' Verna reproved gently, putting a hand on his dark suited arm. 'Women are going *topless* these days.'

'So it seems.'

Feeling that they were treating her like a bump on a log, Abby put in smoothly: 'Maybe you'd like to give Verna something to drink, Ben. Joe and Gary are playing bartender.'

'Thanks for inviting me to your party, Abby,' Verna said with a smile which even Abby had to admit would be irresistible to any man. 'Can I help with anything?'

'No, thanks. Your mother and Debby have everything under control. They won't even let me into the kitchen.' Abby forced an answering smile, and told herself she didn't care that Ben's arm slid round Verna's waist while his frowning face was still directed at her.

It just went to prove that whatever she wore Ben would still regard her as being a lot less feminine than Verna or the faraway Sylvia ... sighing, she knew that her everyday garb of jeans and top would come foremost to Ben's mind when he thought of her—if he thought of her at all.

Free to enjoy herself now that the last comers had arrived, Abby turned away and was immediately snapped up to dance by Clint Edwards, the neighbouring rancher's son whose fair good looks were emphasised by the black blazer and sparkling white shirt he wore.

'Wow, Abby! I've never seen you look like this before ... you're—different in that dress.' As if to prove his point, his hand moved up to the cool softness of her flesh under the shoulder blade and went caressingly over her back. At the same time his head dipped against her cheek and he whispered in her ear: 'I never realised you were so beautiful.'

Like the foal in whose honour the party was supposedly being given, Abby's head reared up and away from Clint's.

'I'm the same Abby I've always been,' she said coolly.

'But you've been hiding your talents under jeans and tee shirts,' he murmured, pulling her close again with a demanding hold it would have created a fuss to break.

Mentally shrugging, Abby submitted to the warm breath at her cheek, the insinuating closeness of Clint's well-knit body. Men were such fools to be taken in by surface appearances, not seeing the true person underneath the frills and fancies. Yet she felt a traitorous thrill of satisfaction in knowing that Clint, who could have had his choice of any girl in the area and who had never shown a romantic interest in herself before, was now breathing heavily close to her ear.

'Let's get something to drink,' she said brightly when the record ended a moment or two later. 'I'm so thirsty I could die!'

The truth of this was evident in the way she quickly drained the lemon-flavoured drink he brought her, and she drank another almost as quickly, feeling vaguely dizzy when another of the men she had known since childhood claimed her for a dance. To her surprise, his breathing became almost as heavy as Clint's, and she puzzled over this while her steps automatically followed his. What was with them all tonight? Simply wearing a dress could make her the target of laboured breathing and whispered suggestions about a trip further into the garden?

She had lost count of the partners clamouring for her dances, slaking her thirst liberally between times and aware more and more of Ben's disapproving frown wherever she went. His own partners ranged from several dances with Verna to duty turns round the patio with the few older ladies Abby had invited. And all the time his opaque green eyes were fastened on her each time she looked up until at last he came across to where she was sipping between dances and took the glass from her hand.

'Will you dance with me, Abby?'

Without waiting for a reply, his long fingers fastened on her hand and pulled her none too gently out to the patio. If the pace of the music had been more lively, she could have concentrated on the movements of her feet, but the slow strains coming from the stereo demanded nothing more than the lazy shuffle of her feet to match the lethargic rhythm of his. His arm completely circled her waist and lay on the faintly defined lines of her ribcage, his head coming down by degrees to rest against the scented softness of her red-gold hair. For a long time they moved so, and Abby felt sleepily that she could stay in that position for ever. The sweetness of Phil's flowers surrounding the patio was woven inextricably in her senses with the sharp pungency of the cologne on Ben's cheek, the warm closeness of his maleness, the hard feel of his shoulder under her pliant fingers.

'Hey, Abby!' Clint was suddenly there beside them, the

faint weaving of his well-made figure betraying that he had made too many trips to the improvised bar in the living room. The hands he put on Abby's bare shoulders were unpleasantly hot. 'When are you going to dance with me again?'

'Not now, pal,' Ben answered tersely for her, and moved Abby so that Clint's hands fell away from her then, when they reached the patio steps to the garden, Ben took Abbey's hand and dragged her into the privacy of a moonlit arbour beyond two guardian ornamental cedars where they were cut off from the view of the dancers.

CHAPTER EIGHT

PLEASURE rippled through Abby, the kind of pleasure she had only recently become aware of. Ben had brought her here away from prying eyes so that he could kiss her ... tonight there would be no holdbacks, no barriers ... she knew now that she loved Ben, wanted him in the way that only an awakened woman could want a man. She would cook for him, sew for him, scrub floors for him ... if only he loved her too.

'What the hell do you think you're doing, Abby?'

'Wh-what?' Abby's half-upstretched arms froze at the harsh timbre in his voice, dropping lifelessly then to her sides.

His hand waved eloquently over her dress and tenderly white shoulders. 'Getting yourself up in an outfit like that!'

She gasped, disappointment bringing an angry tremor to her voice when she threw up at his disturbed face: 'Make up your mind, Ben! First you tell me I'm unfeminine because I don't wear dresses, and when I do——'

'For God's sake, Abby, do you always have to go from one extreme to the other?' he exploded in exasperation, one hand running through the thickest part of his hair. 'There's a happy medium between looking like an under-sized ranch hand and a ...' He bit off the rest of his words and Abby looked coldly up at him.

'None of my friends seem to mind that I look like a—whatever you were about to call me,' she told him frigidly.

'I'll bet they don't!' he muttered thickly, and jerked her to him with a sudden rough motion that made her stumble on the unaccustomed height of her heels and throw her weight against the dark wool of his suit. 'Would you like

112

me to show you what every one of your so-called friends was thinking of when he stood in line to dance with you?'

His eyes glittered narrowly in the moonlight shafting across the garden, also giving his complexion a paler hue and making hollows under his cheekbones. The anger raging inside him was explicit in the deepened lines beside his closely held mouth, and Abby felt a trickle of fear along her spine—fear that had an underlying shiver of expectancy ...

'Don't you dare, Ben Franklin!' she cried unsteadily as resolve hardened in his eyes.

'That's one sure way of making me do something,' he muttered from above her uplifted face, his eyes sweeping abrasively over hers which were darkened to velvet midnight blue, then to her hair that still flamed in the softened quality of moonlight, coming to rest at last on her indignantly parted lips.

Before she had time to close them he had covered them with his own, one hand sliding down over the smoothness of her back to hold her in a vice-like grip, the other moving spasmodically over the cool softness of her shoulder to her throat before his fingertips traced a searing path to the deep valley between her breasts, lingering there as if Ben was satisfying himself that her heartbeat was fluctuating as wildly as he suspected.

Tremors of shock receded in Abby and were replaced by wave upon wave of ice-edged anger. She had wanted Ben to kiss her ... but not like this, as if he was punishing her with all the harsh arrogance of his maleness. Without consciously planning the action, when she felt the soft part of his lower lip against her teeth she closed them with a decisive snap, hearing his muffled oath as his head jerked upwards. Blood spurted darkly on his lip as he looked down at her with white-faced fury, and terror flooded her veins when she saw the murderous glint in his eyes.

'You little hellcat!' he ground out through his teeth, long fingers suddenly at her throat as if he meant to squeeze the life out of her. But instead he kissed her again, savagely and with no heed for the blood welling from his lip, blood that tasted salty on Abby's tongue.

Knowing that however many times she lacerated his mouth he would still continue to kiss her, she gave in to the sudden relaxation of tension and sagged against him, feeling the smoothly woven wool of his suit beneath her hands as she clung to him like a drowning person reaching for a piece of flotsam. Even the lessening anger in his mouth as it moved on hers failed to draw a response from her limp body, and at last he released her, catching her to him again when she would have fallen.

His voice was unsteady when he said: 'I guess I under-rated your ability to protect yourself! Nothing's calculated to kill passion as fast as a bite in a vulnerable spot!... no matter how pretty and white the teeth are.'

It was an effort for Abby to collect her strength and pull away from him, and illogically she missed the feel of his arms round her when they left her waist.

'It—it didn't do much to kill yours!'

'That wasn't passion in the way we're talking about,' he returned tightly, feeling in his pocket and bringing out a cigar, lighting it and breathing deeply on the smoke before going on. 'For some reason, Abby, you bring out the worst in me at times. It's almost as if——'

Debby's voice interrupted his from the patio. 'Abby, are you out here?'

Abby realised suddenly that the music had stopped some time ago, and that she should be inside being hostess rather than tangling with Ben Franklin in the garden.

'Coming, Debby!' she called back, and left Ben without a backward glance.

'What in the world are you doing out there on your own?' Debby asked, attractively pink-cheeked in long white A-line dress.

'Oh, I—I just needed some fresh air,' Abby lied. 'Is there something I can do in the kitchen? I feel so badly that——'

'No need to worry. We went ahead and set everything out, and most people have helped themselves from the buffet.'

'Thanks, Debby, you've been great—your mother too.' Abby felt curiously listless as she followed Debby into the house. Maybe if she had had to see to the food herself, she wouldn't have had that hassle with Ben in the arbour. She glanced behind her once or twice, but there was no sign of his prepossessing figure. Was he still out there, finishing his cigar, or had he taken the back way to his bungalow? A mixture of compunction and savage satisfaction battled for supremacy in the thought that Ben hadn't wanted Verna to know why his lip was swollen in such an obvious way. That it had begun to puff up even before Abby left him had been evident, and compassion gained the lead in her feelings.

Taking just a little of the food on a plate, she went to sit with a group which had gravitated to the patio steps, and no one seemed to notice her preoccupation in the general chatter. Verna, she saw, was in the midst of another group standing near the doors, her eyes turning now and then as if searching for someone. Ben?

Lost in her thoughts, Abby started when she realised that everyone was looking at her in surprise, flushing when a chorus of teasing began.

'Why the far-away look in your eyes, Abby?'

'Who's the lucky guy?'

'You mean you didn't ask him to your party?'

Clint, a glass in his hand rather than the coffee cup the others held, came up from behind and sneered: 'Oh, she asked him to her party all right, but he hasn't been around since he pulled her into the bushes a while ago. What did you do with Ben Franklin, Abby?—bury him out there?'

The others, sensing the ugliness behind Clint's slurred words, changed the subject by pulling Abby to her feet and reminding her of the purpose for having the party.

'Where's the foal you're going to christen, Abby? Let's go out there and wet his head.'

'No. No, he's too young ... so many people all at once would frighten him. Let's just drink to his health in the living room.' Forcing a smile to her face, Abby stepped quickly towards the glass doors into the house, breathing thankfully when the others followed her. It was true that the foal would have been scared and Glory upset by the rowdy presence of such a large group ... but more to the

point was the fact that the lights would be on in Ben's
bungalow, giving rise to further speculation on Clint's part.

For the same reason, when she stood apart from the
others in the living room a few minutes later, she raised
her glass and said in a trembling voice: 'I christen the new
foal *Beau*—because he's beautiful.'

To a general murmur of 'Beau' the foal's health was
drunk, and before anyone else could break the silence Debby
stepped forward and said brightly with a backward look at
her sister:

'And there's something else we have to celebrate! Verna
and Darrel have decided not to go ahead with their divorce ... Verna came back yesterday to tie up the loose ends
here before going back to Vancouver to tie a tighter knot
round Darrel!'

In the general surge of pleased congratulations surrounding the radiant Verna, no one noticed that Abby stood as
if turned to stone. Verna was going back to Darrel? What
about Ben? Was his disappearance from the party due to
the news Verna had imparted to him last night and not, as
Abby had thought, because of that scene in the garden?

The party lasted little more than an hour longer, and
Abby refused Debby's and her mother's help with the
dishes. 'Indeed you won't! That's something I can do in the
kitchen without messing it up.' She hugged Mrs Warner and
Debby in turn. 'I don't know how to thank you both, you've
been wonderful. And,' she smiled into Mrs Warner's tired
blue eyes, 'I'm really pleased about Verna and Darrel. I
can imagine how happy you are that they're getting together again.'

Mrs Warner smiled and nodded tranquilly. 'Yes, I am.
But then I always knew they would. Verna's been awfully
unhappy since they parted, and Darrel has too, I understand.'

But Verna hadn't been so downhearted that she hadn't
strung Ben along in the belief that she was to be a free
woman and open to his advances. Oddly, instead of feeling deliriously happy that Verna was no longer in the
picture, Abby felt only compassion for Ben. Compassion

mixed with guilt that her own actions tonight must have compounded his misery.

Debby whispered as she followed her mother to the door, everyone else having left: 'At least now you have a clear field with Ben! What happened to him anyway? He disappeared halfway through the evening.'

'He—he wasn't feeling well,' Abby returned, not really lying because when she had left Ben in the garden he had looked far from well, although she hadn't known the real reason for his white-faced anguish then.

When she had waved Debby and her mother off, Abby went back into the house, switching lights off as she went and leaving only the normal dim sidelight on in the hall. Strangely, she didn't feel tired, and doing the dishes tonight would abolish the prospect of rising to them in the morning.

After filling the sink with hot soapy water, she made several trips to and from the big kitchen table for the dishes Mrs Warner had stacked there. Debby's words came back to haunt her as she washed and rinsed mechanically. The field would never be clear for Ben to love her ... he must hate her for what she had done to him tonight. And even if that hadn't happened, Abby could never be the kind Ben would fall in love with. He was drawn to sweetly feminine girls like Verna who, she suspected, was a replica of his brother's wife, Sylvia, the one he had loved hopelessly for a long time. Only a similar type to Sylvia could make him forget her ... certainly Abby Mackenzie was far from being that type. What had he called her? A 'hellcat'— no man ever fell in love with a girl he thought of in those terms. And knowing that she was given to biting when provoked, he'd probably never kiss her again, even as a temporary substitute for the kind of girl she was not.

Big tears of self-pity rolled down her cheeks and mingled with the dishwater. She wasn't like that really, not deep down inside her where the wellspring of her being lay, the soft and tremulously tender parts she had hidden even from herself until Ben stirred them and brought them to light. But he would never know what lay beneath the outer layer of spirited independence, the woman who wanted—needed

—the strong arm of love in her life.

Her hands ceased their movements in the water and she stared unseeingly at the taps. Why shouldn't she go and tell him how she felt? At least she could apologise for her unpardonable behaviour earlier. After all, he had only been trying to show her the folly of wearing a dress that left little to a man's imagination while encouraging him to ...

Leaving the remainder of the dishes to soak, Abby sped along to her bedroom. She wouldn't offend Ben's eyes by going to him in the dress that had sparked off their exchange in the first place. Quickly, she threw it off and donned her more normal jeans and warm sweater.

It hadn't occurred to Abby that Ben might already be asleep, and her heart sank a few minutes later when she rounded the corner from the main house and saw that the bungalow was in darkness. Disappointment seeped through her as she stood in front of the blankly unwelcoming front door, the plate of sandwiches she had brought as her excuse wobbling dangerously as her arm lost its elasticity.

The whole ranch was steeped in moon-drenched night, the buildings illuminated with an eerie replica of daylight, and Abby shivered as she looked round the familiar lay-out which seemed suddenly strange. Telling herself that she had never seen the ranch at this in-between time of late night and early morning by herself, she turned to go back to the house. A scrabbling movement in the brush behind the barn brought her head round in quick alarm, and she thought she heard the muted sound of men's voices from that direction, the shadowy speck of figures racing across the meadow behind the barn.

Imagination, she jeered inwardly, but quickened her pace until an alarmed whinny came from the end of the barn where Glory and her foal were housed. Whatever was lurking around, Glory had heard it too, so it wasn't entirely the product of her own overwrought imagination. Retracing her steps, Abby set the plate of sandwiches down on Ben's front step and made her way across to the barn ... her presence would reassure the mare.

Halfway across the yard another, higher-pitched, whinny

reached her ears at the same time as the acrid fumes of the worst hazard a rancher could face assailed her nostrils. Smoke! Her feet scarcely touched the ground as she traversed the rest of the space to the barn and dragged open one of the big double doors. Horrified, her eyes took in the orange-red flames licking greedily at the tinder-dry back wall near Glory and her foal, the smoke already beginning to rise in a spiral from the hay rack at the rear of the stall.

Scarcely hearing the hysterical cries of the mare or the plaintive echoes from her offspring, Abby leapt across to the bolted gate confining the animals. For several seconds her hands scrabbled at the normally loose-fitting bolt, then she bent with a startled exclamation to examine it. It had been wired with closely coiled firmness to the sturdy gate-post, and Abby knew after one glance that she would never be able to unravel it herself in time. For one heat-seared moment her eyes met the half-crazed look in Glory's, and in another she was coughing her way back out of the barn. She had to get Ben . . . he would know what to do.

The bungalow was still in darkness when she ran across to it, and she made no attempt to knock on the door before throwing it open, groping for the light switch then dashing through the house to the bedroom area. The first room she tried was unused, and she sobbed as she turned the handle of the other bedroom door and saw Ben's still figure on the double bed. There was reassurance in the mere sight of his broad torso, bare to where a single sheet straddled his waist, but Abby had no time to appreciate masculine grace or lack of it as she ran across to the bed and shook the smoothly contoured shoulder.

'Ben!' she cried, her breath seemingly lost between barn and bungalow, 'Ben! Wake up! Please wake up, Ben!'

His eyes, when they opened, seemed instantly alert although a frown etched its way between them as he looked up into her face. 'Abby? What are you——? What's wrong?'

'The barn,' she gasped, tugging at his arm. 'It's on fire and—Glory and the foal—oh, please come!'

He made a swift movement with his hand towards the sheet covering him, then stopped abruptly. 'Wait for me in the living room, I'll be right with you.'

Knowing that the rest of him must be as unclothed as the top half, Abby stumbled away and was half way back to the barn when he caught up with her, his dark-coloured jeans and white tee-shirt showing no signs of the speed with which they had been put on.

'Stay out here!' he commanded tersely as they reached the barn doors where the flames from inside sent an ominous glow of smoky orange on to the aged wood.

'But Glory ...' she began, and paused as the sound of splintering wood came to them. 'She's breaking down the gate! It's wired shut, Ben,' she called after him as he ducked through the door and disappeared.

For another minute the regular beat of hoofs on shattering wood came, then a terrified cry was torn from her own throat when a high-pitched scream she had never before heard from any animal rent the air and made even the fierce crackling of the consuming fire seem like a soothing background symphony. Abby rushed to the barn door and saw Ben staggering towards her, a bundle in his arms she recognised as the foal when he came nearer.

'Glory!' she screamed, rushing past Ben, when one arm shot out to spin her round and face her in the opposite direction before grasping the colt again.

'Get out, Abby! There's nothing we can do for Glory.'

'No! No! I have to help her!'

She was part way back into what was now a raging inferno when Ben, without the foal, caught her up in his arms and carried her, kicking furiously, back to the relative coolness of the night air where Joe and several of the other men had gathered in open mouthed horror to gaze at the blazing barn.

'Take the foal and put him with the other horses,' Ben instructed briskly. 'Then see what you can do about stopping the fire spreading to the other buildings—the barn can't be saved.'

'Glory!' Abby screamed again, and tried to leap from the restraining arms, but Ben walked inexorably towards the bungalow. Once there, he set Abby down on her feet in the living room, but kept a firm hold on her waist.

'There's nothing we can do for Glory now, Abby,' he repeated with controlled gentleness.

'You could have saved her,' she raved, pummelling his chest with her clenched fists. 'You could have—you just walked away and left her to burn! I hate you, Ben Franklin! Why did you ever come here?'

Through the tears blinding her eyes she saw the hard cast of his jaw, the soot-streaked marks on his forehead and cheeks, even smelled the smoky singeing on his hair. And under all that, the stress that seemed to have made new lines round his eyes and mouth, the pulse that jumped erratically at his temple.

He pushed her from him abruptly and went to the kitchen, where a moment later she heard the chink of bottle on glass. Coming back to her, he thrust a glass half filled with whisky into her nerveless hands.

'Sit down and drink that,' he told her harshly. 'I'm going back to help the men confine the fire, but I want to see you when it's over.'

Without another word he went from the bungalow and she watched with dazed eyes as his broad shoulders, outlined against the fiercely burning barn, went to where the other men were damping down the grass and wood rail fence adjoining the barn.

Sickened at the sight of Glory's funeral pyre, Abby dropped to the sofa under the window and cried wrenchingly into the whisky she swallowed without thinking. Had Glory known that Abby had let her down? That she might have been able to save her if Ben hadn't stopped her from going back? Again and again the sight of those crazed eyes rose up before Abby until she closed hers and leaned back against the padded arm of the sofa, drawing her legs up close to her body. Poor Glory . . . poor motherless foal . . . poor Ben . . .

'Poor Ben,' she murmured in the seconds before she forced her eyes open and stared bewilderedly up at the tall form looming beside her before switching her gaze to surroundings that were familiar yet strange. What was she doing sleeping in Ben's bungalow? Her eyes came back to the compassionate gleam in his. 'I must have fallen asleep.'

'I'm sorry, Abby,' he said, straightening her legs gently and sitting beside her. 'It took a little longer than I thought to damp down the fire.'

'Fire?' she echoed dazedly, her eyes seeking his until memory rushed back and sent her head sideways into the sofa back. Glory! Glory had been burned horribly ... needlessly. 'Why wouldn't you let me go back for her?' she asked accusingly in a half muffled tone. 'I could have saved her.'

His fingers probed gently for her chin and turned her face back to his. 'No, Abby, you couldn't have. It was already too late when I stopped you. She'd kicked open enough space for the foal to get through, but she ...' Ben paused, his teeth pressing with what must have been painful sharpness on the noticeable swelling on his lower lip. Tightly, he went on: 'There was an upright splinter. She reared and ... came down on it. It killed her almost instantly, so don't torture yourself by thinking you let her down.' Grimness deepened the tired grooves round his mouth. 'Whoever tied up the gate did that.'

A shudder of horror had shaken Abby when he described how Glory had died, but now her breath caught sharply in her throat as she looked up at him through tears.

'Who ... who could have wanted to ... hurt Glory that badly?'

Ben's eyes hardened and he shook his head. 'It wasn't Glory they wanted to hurt—it was you, and maybe me as well.'

'But why?—who? ...'

'I can make a pretty accurate guess,' he said, anger turning his eyes to pale grey. 'But this time, Abby, I'm taking it out of your hands. Human lives could have been lost, so the police have to be told.'

'You mean—*Dave* did this?' she whispered, tears forgotten as her eyes widened in disbelieving wonder. 'But—why?'

His dry chuckle held no mirth. 'Because we stopped what had been a very lucrative sideline for him—siphoning off Cedar Hills cows for his own benefit. As well as losing his opportunity to marry you and get his hands on the whole outfit.'

'Glory's dead just because of *that*? He knew I'd never have married him, whatever happened. It was just that— that Dad wanted to make sure there'd be a *man* to take care of me when he was gone. That's what Dave said. Oh, God ...' she put trembling hands up to cover her face, 'Glory was the one living thing who loved me no matter what ... and I loved her so much.'

Suddenly she was gathered into Ben's arms, her own pushed round his waist, her head cradled against his chest, his hand against her hair holding it there with fierce protectiveness while his lips murmured words of comfort close to her cheek.

'I know you did, honey ... she knew it too ... and you still have her little one ... you'll love him just as much in time ... and never forget that there are people who love you, too ...'

Her head shook negatively against his hand. 'No. Not like that ...'

The hand caressing her back was stilled suddenly, and Ben's body seemed to tense against her. 'Yes. Exactly like that—no matter what.'

Sobs caught in her throat and she was aware all at once of the acrid odour of smoke coming from his tee-shirt, the warm hardness of his muscled chest, the quickened beat of his heart under her ear. Raising her head, she looked searchingly into the dirt-streaked face so near to hers, wonder widening her eyes when at last he turned his head to meet her look and hold to it in the pulsating silence until he gave a forced smile and said:

'Harry loves you that way, doesn't she? And Phil. Most of the men at your party seemed willing to become more important to you if you'd let them.' He put her away from him and stood up, looking down at her with a faintly rueful smile. 'But maybe you should have a warning sign hung round your neck—one that says "I bite when kissed!"'

Hot colour seeped under her paled skin. 'I—I'm sorry about that, Ben. I don't know what got into me.'

'Don't you? It's the same thing that's been eating you for years, Abby.' He frowned. 'But now isn't the time to go into it. Dawn's been in the sky for an hour or more, and it's time you went to bed.'

Stooping suddenly, he lifted her easily from the sofa and went to the door. 'And thanks for your peace-offering of sandwiches—they'll just hit the spot.'

He paused in the doorway and Abby saw that the plate of sandwiches, covered with plastic wrap, had been taken from the step and put on the table.

'Would you like me to make some coffee to go with them?' she asked in a small voice.

'No, you're going to bed,' he said in a decisive tone. 'I'm quite capable of making my own coffee.'

Dawn was indeed streaking in a pink, yellow and blue arc across the eastern sky when he walked with her to the main house, and Abby, though aware that she was perfectly able to manage under her own steam, tightened her hold round his neck. In his enumeration of the people who loved her, he hadn't included himself. But that was no more than she expected after her primitive reaction to his kiss, though that knowledge did nothing to alleviate the lump of despair blocking her heart. If only she had known about Verna then, her reaction would have been entirely different. She would have understood and made allowances for Ben's anger, which hadn't been directed at her dress at all but in an abstract way at Verna.

She kept her arms round his neck when he laid her on top of her neatly made bed and he looked questioningly into her contrite eyes.

'Ben, I—I'm sorry ... about your lip ... and about Verna——'

'Verna?'

'That she's going back to Darrel. I know that's why you were so mad at me for wearing that dress.'

Her arms were disengaged with firm hands. 'How I felt about your dress was nothing to do with Verna,' he said concisely, a frown ridging his brows as he looked down at her. 'As for her getting together with her husband, I'm more than glad she took my advice and——'

'*Your* advice!'

'Certainly. I have very strong feelings about divorce—and even stronger ones about being used in the hopeless cause of Verna trying to forget her husband.'

'But all those dinners she made for you——'

A wince passed over his weary features. 'They were all part of my campaign to persuade her to do what she wanted to do anyway. That man owes me a considerable debt!' A light smile touched his mouth. 'But maybe not—it was nice having the feminine touch in the house for a while. Makes a man think he should be settling down and have a woman to come home to on a permanent basis.'

'Somebody like Verna, I suppose—or Sylvia.'

His eyes narrowed sharply. 'Something like them, yes,' he nodded, then half turned away. 'Remind me to tell you about Sylvia some time. You could learn a lot from her.'

'No, thanks,' Abby returned tartly, sitting up and swinging her feet to the floor, her mood of sentimental contrition gone. 'I'm not really interested in the women in your love life—especially when one of them happens to be married to your brother.'

He looked long at her figure, drooping now with tiredness, and seemed about to say one thing when he sighed heavily and substituted another. 'Get some sleep, Abby. I'll see you later.'

Long strides took him to the door and Abby's lower lip trembled when the white-panelled wood had closed behind him. Verna was out of the picture—had never been in it, according to Ben—but Sylvia was still there and always would be. His ideal woman, the one who would never be available to him because he felt strongly about divorce and would never ask her to break up her marriage to his brother.

Lying under the covers a few minutes later, she reflected sleepily that it wouldn't have mattered anyway if Sylvia didn't exist for him ... it was growing more and more clear that Abby Mackenzie was the last woman in the world he would choose as the feminine type he would like to come home to on a permanent basis.

CHAPTER NINE

ABBY woke reluctantly at noon when a hand gently shaking her shoulder penetrated her consciousness. Blinking, she looked up at the familiar face flushed red with excitement.

'Harry!' she exclaimed, sitting up and blinking away the last vestiges of sleep. 'Where did you come from?'

'From Kamloops, of course—where we should have left days ago! Oh my, Abby, what a terrible thing to have happened and us down there not knowing a thing about it till Ben phoned.'

'Ben phoned you?'

'Yes, and I'd have been really mad if he hadn't! Oh Abby, I'm so sorry about Glory, I know how much she meant to you. Phil feels as badly as I do about the whole thing, and wishes he had been here to do something to help.'

'He couldn't have done anything,' Abby said mechanically as she patted the older woman's arm, gladder than she had ever been to have her reassuring presence in the house again. 'Even Ben couldn't save the barn ... but he and the men managed to confine the fire just to there, so there was no other damage.'

'If I could catch that Dave Corben I'd wring his neck with my own hands,' Harry said with unaccustomed bloodthirstiness, then she gave a start of remembrance. 'That brings to mind that there's a policeman who wants to talk to you in the living room.'

'A policeman?' Abby echoed. 'You mean Ben called them already?'

'Early this morning. I've brought you some coffee—the sergeant can wait till you've had that.' Harry went to the door, 'I won't waste time talking now, honey, there'll be lots of that later.'

'Thanks, Harry, for the coffee—and for coming so quickly. Things seem so much better now you're here.'

'Ben said you'd feel that way,' the housekeeper returned complacently, frowning as she added: 'Though if you'd told me about the party I would have been here to help.'

But then I wouldn't have been doing dishes in the kitchen at that late hour, Abby thought, sipping her coffee when Harry had gone. And I certainly wouldn't have been taking sandwiches to Ben as an excuse to apologise, so the fire would not have been noticed until it was too late to save even the foal. The thought of the motherless little animal brought a lump to her throat and she put down the coffee with a clatter and rose quickly. Glory's offspring was the one thing she couldn't bear to think about so soon. As for the police sergeant in the living room, he would have to wait a little longer until she had showered and dressed.

Looking remarkably fresh in blue floral overblouse and navy slacks, she went along to the living room fifteen minutes later. Ben was standing by the wide window chatting quietly with the uniformed police officer, who was on a par with Ben as far as height went, though there the resemblance ended. His light blond hair was brushed neatly back over a fair skinned face and pale blue eyes, his figure heavy though giving an impression of hardbound muscle rather than superfluous flesh. The blue eyes were kindly when Ben introduced them. The sergeant was unfamiliar to her, so she knew that he must be from another detachment than the local one.

'Sergeant Mathers . . . Abby Mackenzie. The sergeant just wants to ask you a few questions about last night, Abby.'

Abby noticed now that, although Ben had showered and shaved and changed into clean clothes, his face was drawn with tiredness. But when she mentioned this in a low voice as they all went to sit down, he told her impatiently that he was all right.

'I'll be as quick as I can, Miss Mackenzie,' the policeman began, settling himself into an armchair by the fireplace when Abby sat down at one end of the sofa. Ben dropped into the chair opposite the sergeant's and shaded his eyes from the bright light pouring in through the un-curtained window.

'First I'd like to tell you how sorry I am about your horse. I understand she was a valuable animal.'

'Yes, she was given to me by my father,' Abby said quietly. 'But she had more than just monetary value to me.'

'Of course. Well, we'll do our best to pin down the person, or persons, who did this. Have you any idea, any suspicion, as to who would have had reason to destroy the animal? That was obviously the idea when the stable gate was wired shut.'

'Well, I——' Abby hesitated and looked quickly at Ben, but his hand completely covered his eyes now as if he had fallen asleep. Had he voiced his suspicions to the sergeant? She took a deep breath and told the policeman about Dave Corben probably being the guilty party.

'And why would this Dave Corben want to get at you in this way? Was he upset at being replaced by Mr Franklin here?'

'Yes ... yes, he was upset about that, but——' she hesitated again and cast another look at the unsupportive Ben, wishing they had had a chance to corroborate their stories before talking with the police sergeant. Turning back to the uniformed man who was regarding her with a blandly shrewd look, she went on quickly:

'We—that is, Mr Franklin found out that Dave had been —stealing Cedar Hills cattle and selling them on his own account.'

'And you faced him with this?'

'Yes ... we went out and waited for them one night——'

'Them?'

'Wally Penman was there too. He was one of the ranch hands—Dave hired him a couple of years ago. There was another man, the one driving the truck, but I didn't see much of him. I don't think I'd ever seen him before.'

Sergeant Mathers sighed. 'Well, there's your motive—you cut off their access to easy income.' The blue eyes sharpened to hard points. 'Tell me, Miss Mackenzie—why didn't you inform the detachment at that time? If you had, your horse might be alive today.'

'I know,' she whispered miserably. 'Ben—Mr Franklin—wanted to at the time, but I——' she bit her lip nervously, 'I didn't want that kind of publicity.' Haltingly, she explained about the Wests and her unwillingness to let them think she couldn't run the ranch herself.

'Cattle stealing doesn't usually make the front page of national dailies,' the sergeant remarked drily, closing the brown notebook he had been holding on his knee while he jotted down a word or two here and there during the interview. When he rose, Ben's hand came down from his eyes and Abby realised he hadn't been asleep at all ... he had been listening very closely to what she said. 'We'll get on to it, Miss Mackenzie, and see what we can do. You'll be hearing from us.'

Abby followed him to the front door. 'What—what's going to happen to Dave when you find him?'

He shrugged and put on his hat, which made him look remote suddenly. 'What he did could have had very serious consequences—if there'd been a wind, and it was in the right direction, the whole ranch could have been burned out. You were very lucky.'

Ben came over to stand beside them, handsome in dark green shirt and similarly coloured slacks despite the channels of tiredness running from nose to mouth.

'I've just remembered something else,' Abby said, slowly thoughtful. 'I saw two figures running away from the barn last night just before I heard Glory and smelled the smoke.'

'Did you recognise these figures?' the sergeant asked sharply.

She shook her head. 'No, they were too far away, and they cut away across the pasture behind the barn. I guess that's not too much help to you, is it?'

'It could be. We might find car tracks over there somewhere. You had so many cars out front last night for your party it would be impossible to trace individual marks. Nothing else you remember?'

'No.'

'Well, if you think of anything give us a call.' Turning back from the door as he opened it, the policeman looked down at Abby, the kindly light back in his eyes. 'Why don't you give these Wests a chance? They might be more than willing to help you out—this is a big place for a girl to run on her own.'

'I'll let them know what's happened, of course,' Abby said stiffly.

There was an almost imperceptible shrug of the well-set shoulders and a touch of fingers to his hat before the sergeant turned to look levelly at Ben and give him a tight nod.

'Why did you sit there like a dummy all the time he was questioning me?' Abby demanded angrily as Ben turned back into the hall.

'Because he made that a condition for letting me stay in the room,' he returned mildly. 'Usually they interview people separately.'

'I thought they only did that with criminals!' Abby said with an indignant rise in her voice. Catching sight of the telephone in the hall as they passed it, she went on slowly: 'I suppose I should let the Wests know—after all, it's partly their property until the debt's paid off.' She hadn't realised how reluctant she sounded until Ben said quietly:

'Would you like me to call them?'

'No . . . no, of course not,' she denied quickly. 'It seems—cowardly to let you do my dirty work.'

Unexpectedly, his hand came out to lift her chin. 'If there's anything you're not, Abby Mackenzie, it's a coward,' he said softly, no vestige of mockery in his light green eyes. His voice became more normal when he went on: 'I don't mind doing it, and it might come better from a third party. You're not exactly overflowing with the milk of human kindness where the Wests are concerned!'

'I've no reason to be,' she returned smartly, then noticed his weariness again. 'You're tired, Ben, I'll do it myself.'

His voice was firm and brooked no argument. 'It should only take five minutes. If you'll let me have the key, I'll phone from the office on my way to bed.'

'You didn't get any sleep at all?'

Shrugging, he said: 'There wasn't much point after I left you. I knew the police would be here not long after I called them.' He smiled tiredly. 'The sandwiches were good.'

'Oh, I'm glad.' Unusual shyness sent a rosy glow to her cheeks, and she turned away to get the office key, saying as she handed it to him: 'Have a good rest, Ben—and come here for dinner tonight.'

'It's a date—if you'll promise not to serve pickled walnuts!'

'I just happen to have some,' she twinkled back and felt guiltily conscious as she went to join Harry in the kitchen that she should have done the telephoning herself. Mingled with that feeling was one of warm contentment that she had Ben, for however long he stayed at Cedar Hills, to deal with the Wests for her.

Another thought struggled for recognition at the back of her mind, but it eluded the finger she tried to put on it at that moment.

Abby was laying the receiver back on its cradle that evening when Ben announced his presence at the front door. Colour came and went in her cheeks as she went to let him in. Would he mock the dress she had unearthed in her closet, one of such high-necked virginal whiteness that it was a complete contrast to the electric blue she had worn last night? Dresses were almost non-existent in her wardrobe, and this was one she had forgotten about though it still fitted her perfectly. Putting one sleeveless arm out to the door, she knew she would be able to tell at once from his eyes what he thought of it.

Surprise registered first, followed by a smile that held no trace of mockery as his gaze went down the figure hugging style to where it ended at her knees then travelled on to her sheer stockinged legs made even more slender by the white heeled sandals she wore.

'You look—beautiful, Abby,' he said softly, genuine admiration smiling from his eyes and sending quivers along her spine.

'I don't usually wear dresses, as you know,' she said almost brusquely in instinctive defence. 'But Harry likes it when I do on Sundays.'

He followed her into the hall, and now there was a tinge of amusement in his voice. 'Good for Harry. Though I think it's wrong for her to restrict it to Sundays. You're provocative in the jeans you have to wear around the ranch, but a knockout in a dress.'

She turned to face him indignantly. 'What do you mean, "provocative"?'

'You've never walked away from yourself, so you wouldn't know,' he grinned with such a boyish air that her attention was drawn to the relaxed, rested outlines of his features. The swelling on his lip had gone down considerably and was scarcely noticeable, she was glad to note.

When the import of his words penetrated, she blushed furiously and spun round to walk into the living room. 'That was—Sergeant Mathers on the phone,' she said to cover her trembling embarrassment.

'And?'

'They picked up Dave—and Wally—heading south this afternoon. They were taken to Kamloops for questioning, and being held there while the police investigate further.'

'I'd have thought it was pretty obvious they're guilty,' Ben pointed out, 'if they were making a run for it.' He came and stood near to where she was sitting beside the fireplace but didn't sit down.

'Dave told them that he and Wally were on their way to a big ranch south of Kamloops to get jobs there.' Abby looked up at him, distress darkening her eyes. 'It's all so horrible, I wish they'd just let them go. Punishing them won't bring Glory back.'

'But it might prevent the same thing happening again elsewhere,' he remarked logically, then indicated the bottles on a side table. 'Mind if I pour a drink?'

'Of course not,' Abby half rose hastily, but he waved her back. 'I'm sorry, I'm not being a very good hostess, am I?'

'You're a very lovely one tonight,' he said simply. 'Can I get you something?'

'A—a dry sherry, please.'

The drink warmed and soothed her as she sipped it, and Ben's relaxed figure opposite, his capable hands caressing the short glass containing whisky and soda, seemed completely at home there. If only it could be like this more often when they were together, instead of the running battle they indulged in at most of their encounters. They might be a married couple having a casual drink before dinner, and that thought sped the wine on its way through her veins with a warm glow.

'Oh, I almost forgot—you phoned the Wests?'

'Yes.'

'Well?' Curiosity tinged the eagerness in her voice and she saw his eyes fall to the amber liquid in his glass. 'What are they like?'

He shrugged. 'They sound just like people—ordinary people. They were concerned about you after last night.'

'I bet they were!' Abby snorted derisively. 'More likely they were concerned about their investment in the ranch! Did they say anything about sending somebody out here to take over from my incompetent hands?'

'No.' Ben looked at her strangely, almost accusingly. 'As I said they were concerned about you ... they seemed to think I could cope with any other emergencies that come up.'

'I'm glad,' she said with such fervour that his brows lifted in surprise.

'Are you? I thought I was considered on a par with the Wests.' His eyes glinted as he gave her a faintly ironic smile.

'Well, in some ways, maybe,' she returned honestly, 'but you don't patronise me in the same way they do, or as my ...' she faltered to a stop and turned her eyes to the empty fireplace.

'As your father did?' Ben finished for her gently.

Her lashes remained lowered on her cheeks. 'Dad was always disappointed that he didn't have a son to take over the ranch.'

'And you tried to be that son for him?' he suggested, his voice holding a quality she wasn't quite sure of so that she raised her eyes to look at him defensively.

'There's nothing wrong in a man wanting a son, is there?'

'No,' he admitted. 'Especially a rancher. But he doesn't have to let his daughter know her birth was a disappoint-

ment to him. And are you even sure it was a disappointment? If he'd really wanted a son, he could have married
again.'

Abby's breath drew in sharply. 'He'd never have done
that! No other woman could have taken my mother's
place.'

'No, I suppose not,' Ben sighed with such heartfelt sincerity that Abby knew he was thinking of his own love for
Sylvia, a love no other woman could replace, and it was
with a sense of relief that she heard Harry say:

'If you've finished your drinks, I'll serve dinner now.'

Abby had asked her and Phil to join Ben and herself at
the table, but Harry had refused adamantly, saying Abby
and the foreman would have a lot to talk over.

But it was Ben who supplied most of the conversation,
regaling her with awesome and sometime hilarious tales
of his experiences in Texas as if he was intent on banish-
ing the lingering sadness she felt at Glory's death. So she
saw yet another side of his character, a side she hadn't
even suspected of existing. Interesting, too, were the snip-
pets of information he gave her about his young life,
pieces which added up to a complete picture of family
warmth and love.

'It's strange, isn't it,' Abby mused as she stirred her
coffee after the meal, 'that your father had so many sons,
and mine would have been happy to have just one.'

'It works out the other way, too. My father wanted a
daughter he could spoil, but he had to put up with us four
boys. Now he has to be content with the wives they bring
home.'

A shadow crossed Abby's eyes, and she couldn't stem
the sarcastic flow of words to her lips. 'And does Sylvia
enjoy being spoiled by her father-in-law?'

'It would be hard to imagine Sylvia being spoiled by anyone—though my brother's tried hard enough to do that
since they've been married.'

'He loves her a lot?' Although she knew she was probably
turning a knife in the wound of his own love for his
brother's wife, she couldn't resist doing so.

Slowly, consideringly, Ben said: 'Let's say that if he lost her for any reason, his own life wouldn't be worth living any more.'

Abby subsided into her chair with a barely perceptible sigh. *For any reason*—one reason could be his wife's admission of love for his brother. An admission Abby knew Ben would never allow her to make, considering the closeness of the family relationship.

'What about your other brother's wife?'

'Jenny?' Ben smiled with such indulgence that she knew this sister-in-law was one he regarded only with amused brotherly acceptance. 'She's very different from Sylvia—impulsive, harum scarum. John never knows what she'll get up to next, but I guess she's good for him.' He smiled again, wryly. 'He's inclined to be a little too serious about life.' Glancing at his watch, he got to his feet.

'It's after ten, Abby, and you should get to bed. You haven't had much sleep lately.'

Abby followed him to the front door, so abstracted by her thoughts that she scarcely noticed when he took her into his arms in the shadowed hall. The happiness she had felt earlier in the evening had turned to a lead weight in her breast at the very mention of Sylvia. Ben might amuse himself, or find her independence a challenge he had to overcome by kissing her as no one ever had before, but there would never be anything more than that between them. She realised suddenly that Ben was saying huskily into her ear that she should wear dresses more often. Lifting his head, he looked directly into her eyes.

'Girls look so virginal in white,' he mused, 'though most of them who wear it are far from that these days.'

A spark leapt to Abby's eyes and her chin jutted suddenly upward. 'That depends on the kind of girl you—mix with!' she tossed into his half smiling face. '*I'm* a——' she broke off with a startled gasp and swung away from him to hide the colour flooding her neck and cheeks. Ben reached out and caught her by the waist, drawing her back to him and raising her chin with gentle fingers.

'Don't you think I know that?' he said in a husky voice.

'You'd never even been kissed properly until I did that first time.'

Abby swallowed audibly. 'So?' She laughed scornfully. 'Don't fool yourself that because you kissed me that way I'll fall at your feet and beg for more! I'm not entered in the marriage stakes, and if I were, I wouldn't——'

'Under other circumstances, I might try to change your mind about that,' he said, his hands digging into her flesh at either side of her waist. 'But I can't right now. Anyway,' his voice lightened as he smiled whimsically, 'I can't even kiss you since my lip was put out of action last night. Except in token thanks for having me to dinner.'

She felt his lips drop with light pressure to hers and then, before her treacherous senses had time to register more than a beginning response to their touch, he had stood away from her and said 'Goodnight, Abby,' very softly as he opened the door, closing it with what could have been a regretful click behind him.

For several moments she stood there, her fingers coming up to trace the outline of her lips where his had touched them. Then she turned blindly away and went to her room without saying goodnight to Harry and Phil. Not bothering to undress immediately, she threw herself on the bed and stared up at the rose-hued ceiling.

Love had come with stealthy hands to embrace her, taking her unawares with the sinuous fingers of delight that reached deep into the sensuous sleeping area of her body to stir it to vibrant life. A life she had known so little about before Ben came to Cedar Hills ... but it wasn't only the physical effect he had on her. For the first time in her memory, the words he had spoken made sense to her— that there could never be a strictly equal relationship between a man and a woman. Sometimes he would give more, sometimes the onus would be on her ... but in the end it evened out to a harmonious whole.

Abby gave an impatient exclamation and sat up. Why was she wasting time on such thoughts? There could never be any relationship, in whole or in part, between herself and Ben—he had admitted as much tonight. 'Under other circumstances' he could have persuaded her to marry him, he had said. In other words, if he hadn't been so much in love with another woman he might find the effort worthwhile!

No, Mr Franklin, she muttered, rising and taking off the dress he had admired, throwing it savagely at the bottom of her closet, you won't use Abby Mackenzie as a temporary substitute for a woman unavailable to you. Just lay one finger on me again and I'll ...

Breakfast wasn't quite over in the kitchen the next morning when Ben appeared, part of the smile he had given Harry remaining in his eyes as he sought out Abby at the dinette.

'Will you stay and have some breakfast, Ben?' Harry urged with obvious eagerness to return to the frying pans on the stove.

'No, thanks, Harry, I've already eaten. I just want to talk to Abby about the foal.' So saying, he crossed with his customary long strides to take a seat opposite Abby, but made no objection when Harry brought the percolator and a thick mug, pouring coffee for him and replenishing Abby's at the same time.

At mention of the foal, Abby's throat had closed round a painful lump of grief, and she kept her eyes lowered when Ben said with urgent persuasion:

'Abby, the foal won't take a substitute mother ... he's going to have to be fed by hand, and I think you should be the one to do it.'

'No!' Her voice came out in a strangled shrillness. 'I don't even want to see the foal, let alone feed it!' She looked up then and met Ben's eyes, his expression of disgusted incredulity infuriating her further. 'How can you ask me to do something like that after what happened to Glory?'

Ben took a draught of coffee as if he needed it before saying: 'It's not his fault that his mother died. Do you want him to die too?'

'Now, Abby,' Harry came over to insert, 'you know you wouldn't want little Frank to suffer even more than he has to after losing his mother, would you?'

'Frank?' queried Ben, his reddish brown brows lifted

quizzically when Abby glanced at him. She looked quickly back into her coffee cup.

'I—I changed my mind, Harry,' she said in a low voice. 'I decided to call him "Beau" instead.'

Ben's searching gaze burned through her lids, but he made no comment on the change of name except to say quietly: 'Well, Frank or Beau, whatever his name is, has to be fed or he'll die. Will you do it?'

'Why does it have to be me?' Abby cried, rising in confusion. 'Somebody else can do it.'

'He belongs to you,' Ben stated deliberately, getting to his feet and giving Abby a look she didn't like one bit. 'How can you expect somebody else to have the same interest you have in him?'

'Oh, never mind about it now,' Harry put in placatingly. 'Phil can do what needs to be done for the poor little beast till Abby feels more like it.'

'I'll never be able to look at him without thinking of Glory,' Abby choked and rushed from the kitchen, taking with her Ben's coldly disapproving look. Putting up a hand to snatch the key to the office from its hook above the telephone, she exclaimed under her breath when she found it gone. Ben hadn't returned it after phoning the Wests yesterday, so now she would have to face him again.

He was just leaving the kitchen by the back door when she called to him and asked for the keys. Tightlipped, he took them from his jeans pocket and tossed them to her, not even waiting to see if she caught them before striding through the door.

The keys still held his body warmth, and hot tears pricked her eyes as she walked confusedly to the office with them clutched in her hand. It was unfair of him to expect her to see, let alone handle, the foal so soon after Glory had died so horribly in the fire. Trying to feed the young animal would be a constant reminder of the mother he could never replace. How could Ben be so heartless as to insist on it?

Because that was what he was, she told herself tartly, sitting down with a thump behind the desk. Heartless and inconsiderate. He had kissed her with the experience that knew just how to overcome her defences, how to make her newly wakened body crave for more, but what had it meant to him? No more than a chance to prove his superiority as a male, his ability to bend her to his will. Her lips tightened rebelliously. Never again, Ben Franklin, she vowed, wishing suddenly that he would leave Cedar Hills, as he had hinted he might, soon. She had lived contentedly enough before he came, and she could spend the rest of her life the same way.

Pushing away the bleakness that thought brought to her spirit, she threw herself into the paper work she hated.

CHAPTER TEN

HORRIFIED neighbours had rallied round with sympathy and help when news of the fire reached them, and already by the following Tuesday a group of the menfolk were working at clearing away the ashes and rubble of the old barn to make way for the new one they would help build.

Abby walked across the yard at mid-morning with the intention of helping, answering the greetings from the neighbours before setting to and grasping several long pieces of charred rafter and carrying them over to the growing pile of wreckage at the far side of the barn.

'What the hell do you think you're doing?' a low but furious voice came from behind her as she straightened. Her eyes went involuntarily to Ben's naked torso where dark red hair mingled with the grey and white of ashy residue on his chest. His eyes held the Alpine coldness of green lake water. Fortunately, none of the other men was near.

'I'm working on my property—do you mind?' she flared, sidestepping to move past him, but her arm was caught in a fiery grip which did more than words could to signify his anger.

'That's why these men are here,' he gritted. 'They've left their own places to come and help so that you don't have to do it. Now you're throwing their good intentions back in their teeth.'

She stared up at him in wide-eyed amazement. 'How am I doing that? I'd have thought they'd be glad of an extra pair of hands!'

'Not a woman's!' When Abby opened her mouth to protest again he added brusquely: 'I don't have time to go into it now ... but it would be more welcome if you'd do something they can't do for themselves right now.'

140

'What?'

'Make some coffee and something to eat. They'll appreciate that a lot more than any rubble clearing you can do.'

From the sound of his tone, Abby knew that he regarded any efforts she might make in that direction as infinitesimal, but she had no time for further talk, because Ben released her arm with a disgruntled gesture and turned the smooth brown muscles of his back on her as he walked back to the section he had been working.

She glanced round at the other men quickly, but none of them seemed unduly interested in her conversation with Ben, probably thinking that she had simply wanted to have a few words with her foreman. She stood there a moment or two longer until she had to move out of the way of two burly ranchers, like Ben unclothed to the waist so that washing would be a simple matter when the dirty work was done, then she picked her way back to the yard. Hesitating for only a second there to look back mutinously at the knotted muscles on Ben's arms as he lifted a particularly heavy beam, she pivoted on her heel and walked smartly towards the house.

Harry was nowhere to be seen in the kitchen, so Abby got out the huge percolator normally used only for parties, and saw to the coffee before getting three large loaves and bread knife out. She had just begun to slice thickly on the homemade crusty bread when Harry rushed in at the back door, her hair unusually ruffled, her face flushed.

'Oh, Abby, I was just coming to do that. I don't know what those men think of our hospitality!'

Abby continued slicing after a swift look at the housekeeper's agitated features. 'What are you looking so worried about?'

'Nothing. Here, let me do that.'

'I'm quite capable of making a few sandwiches, Harry, and what do you mean, nothing? You're like a hen thrown out of its nest! Come on, out with it.'

'It's the foal,' Harry burst out, her eyes flashing a wary look at the girl's bent head over the bread board. 'No matter how I try, I can't get him to drink the milk.'

Abby's head jerked up. 'I thought Phil was seeing to that.'

The older woman nodded. 'He was, but—well, it's understandable, Abby, he thought he should be helping the men with the barn, not ...' She paused, leaving the rest unsaid, but Abby had no trouble in filling in herself.

'I know,' she sighed impatiently. 'Hand-feeding a foal is woman's work—like making coffee and sandwiches. I've heard it all from Ben Franklin.'

'Did he—' Harry hesitated delicately, '—ask you to make refreshments for the men?'

Abby cut viciously down into the last part of the first loaf. 'The almighty Mr Franklin doesn't *ask*, Harry, he *tells*! Anybody would think this ranch belonged to him!'

'Hmm. Well, I'll get some ham for a filling for those sandwiches, and I think I have a few cold beef slices.' Obviously in her element, Harry bustled over to the refrigerator and poked happily among its contents while Abby started on the second loaf.

The two women managed to carry the large percolator out to the barn, each taking a sturdy side handle, and Abby felt a grudging kind of pleasure when their appearance was greeted with heartfelt appreciation by the men. Two more trips brought the rest of the substantial snack to the scene of operations, and the dirt-streaked men gladly left the work site to perch on machinery and wood piles nearby.

Abby, pouring coffee into sizeable mugs from the makeshift table, trembled slightly, irritating her as Ben, the last to leave the barn, put out a blackened hand to take the coffee. Her lips compressed, she kept her eyes lowered to the tanned beginning of his throat until he said quietly:

'Thanks, Abby. You've saved everybody's life.'

'I'm only following orders,' she bit off sharply, allowing herself one sweeping glance over the penetrating gleam of his green eyes and face streaked with dust and sweat. 'Food's over there.'

'Will you sit with me? There's something I want to ask you to do.'

'Ask? Or tell?'

For a moment the hard line of his jaw tensed, then he said in an even voice: 'Whichever one will get the job done —but I'll try to remember you're my boss.'

Abby poured coffee for herself from the urn and followed him to a pile of used lumber some distance from the others, seating herself with a definite space between them. For a few minutes nothing was said as Ben ate and drank intently, but at last he sighed and wiped his mouth with the back of his hand.

'That was good. There's nothing like homemade bread cut in thick slices when you're hungry—did you make the sandwiches?'

'I cut the bread,' she acknowledged shortly, denying the thrill of pleasure his words gave her, and at the same time wondering why they had sent that warm glow through her. She was no man's slave! 'What did you want to ask me?'

'In a minute.' He stood up, arching his back with a tired motion, and looked down at her empty mug. 'Would there be more coffee in that urn, and would you like some?'

'There is, and I would,' she told him then, realising how ungracious she had sounded, added as she stood up: 'I'll get it—you have to get back to your *man's* work in a while.' Looking up to judge the effect of her irony, she felt a tug of shock at his nearness. The light film of moisture across his bronzed shoulders and chest was clearly visible, and the weakness in her lower limbs that made her want to be crushed against that chest sent her heart palpitating in an uncontrollable way until she looked up into the cool appraisal in his eyes. Knowledge was there, as if he had looked into her mind and knew exactly what her thoughts, her fantasy, had been. As well, there was a faint yet hard gleam of sorrowful disdain far back in his eyes, mockery in his:

'I appreciate your sacrifice of liberated principles.' He smiled, his mouth stretching further over the whiteness of his teeth when she snatched the mug from his hand and walked swiftly away from him. Pouring the coffee and cream and sugar gave her time to collect herself, but her composure was shattered again when she returned to the seated Ben.

'After giving the matter further consideration,' he said

thoughtfully as if they had been discussing something of deadly seriousness, 'I'd say "provocative" was definitely the right word.'

Abby's cheeks flamed with angry colour, and she barely resisted the temptation to throw the hot coffee into his now grinning face. 'That's all men think about, isn't it?' she fumed. '*I* don't spend most of *my* time watching men walking away from me.'

'Don't you?' he insinuated, and her face took on an even deeper colour when the unbidden memory rose in her mind of the flat-hipped grace of his departing figure. He chuckled indulgently and pulled her down by the wrist to sit beside him closer than she had been before so that she felt the hard muscles of his thigh against her softer flesh. 'Don't worry about it, Abby,' he murmured, 'it's the most natural thing in the world for the sexes to admire each other's bodies. It shows you're normal.'

'Thanks a lot for giving me the benefit of your vast experience in these matters,' she snapped sarcastically, and pulled her hand away from his light clasp on it. 'The other men are about to go back to work, so you'd better tell me what it is you want.'

Unperturbed, he continued to smile at her with eyes that had warmed now to the green of tropical waters. Softly, he said: 'What I want from you, you're not ready to give me—yet.'

Her eyes locked with his and his smile grew fainter, disappearing altogether when she made a jerky effort to rise. The hard skin of his work-roughened hand was abrasive on her forearm and she swallowed once before injecting her voice with a tartness she was far from feeling.

'Then don't waste my time and yours! Most of the men are working on the barn, so there's all their normal work to do around the ranch.'

The moment of lightness had gone in the hardening of his eyes, the lifting of his hand from her arm. 'What wasn't done before we started on the barn will be taken care of by a couple of the older men this afternoon. What I wanted to ask you to do right now is to go into town and order up the lumber we need for the new barn.'

'But I've no idea what to order!' she exclaimed, looking up at him aghast.

'I've got it all written down, so all you have to do is hand it over to the clerk in the lumber yard office.'

'Why can't you phone the order in?' she asked suspiciously.

'Because I'm hoping you'll widen those baby blue eyes and have the clerk fall over himself to deliver the lumber in double quick time,' he said, tongue in cheek. 'The quicker it's here, the quicker the new barn will be erected and the quicker the other ranchers can get back to their own places.'

Abby stood up and looked down at him with far from 'baby' blue eyes. 'I'm not in the habit of using my eyes or any other part of me to get what I want,' she flung at him coldly. 'But as I have to go into town anyway, I'll take your list and give it to Curt Hansen. His father owns the lumber yard—and, incidentally, Curt's immune to any attraction in my eyes—he's been looking at them since Grade One in school!'

'Too bad for him—that he can't see them from a stranger's point of view,' Ben added hastily when she bristled again. 'I'll get the list.'

She was watching the lithe movements of his hips beneath taut blue denim as he went to where his shirt hung against a fence post when she remembered his earlier remark and turned away with pink cheeks. At least *she* would never tell *him* that he looked provocative walking away from her, she thought resentfully.

Almost snatching the paper from his hand when he came back, she went over to the table where Harry was for once showing annoyance with Phil.

'You have to do it, Phil, or that poor little creature's going to fade away!'

'I don't see what's so difficult about giving a foal some milk, for heaven's sake,' he grumbled, looking over to where the other men were preparing to start work again. 'There's too much to do here for me to——'

'Don't worry about it, Phil,' Abby told him quietly. 'I'll see what I can do about the foal.'

'Oh, Abby, honey, are you sure you want to?' Harry

asked worriedly. 'I brought up all those children, but he wouldn't have anything to do with me.'

'There's a mite of difference in the technique,' her husband smiled drily, turning to Abby. 'I'd be grateful if you have the time to spend with him, Abby. That's mostly what it takes, time and patience.'

'I can't guarantee the patience,' Abby responded, lifting the empty coffee urn from the table, 'but I have lots of time before lunch. I won't be going into town until this afternoon.'

By the time she looked round, Ben was already rejoining the other men. Had he heard her offer to try her luck with the foal after her adamant refusal the day before? Shrugging slightly, she carried the urn toward the house. From a distance, she found it comparatively easy to bring to mind the hope that Ben Franklin would disappear from her life for ever.

Strangely, Abby's patience far outstripped the time at her disposal. Prepared to feel an illogical resentment at the colt for being alive while her beloved Glory was dead, she was surprised to find that her qualms disappeared the instant she saw the young animal alone in one of the regular stalls in the stable. He had collapsed on the fresh straw piled liberally round him as if too weak to stand on his as yet spindly legs, and the viscid softness of the dark eyes he turned on Abby tugged at her heart.

'Oh, darling baby,' she dropped to her knees beside him and cradled the well-shaped head to her shirt, murmuring soft nothings which he accepted docilely. Her caresses seemed to comfort him, but the milk she tried to give him over and over again he rejected with sideways turns of his head.

'You have to eat, baby,' she said gently, her eyes clouded now with concern at the thought of losing the son as well as the mother. The passing of time brought an ever fiercer determination to save the foal, whose chestnut coat was exactly the shade of Glory's and who promised to be an even finer specimen than his mother had been. But more

important than that was the healing balm that soothed her
spirit and assuaged her grief in the knowledge that one day
this delicately formed colt would at least partially fill the
void left by Glory.

From time to time she refilled the bucket she had brought
in with hot water, keeping the milk at an even temperature
by submerging the container occasionally, but still he refused the alien nourishment she offered him. Almost sob-
bing with frustration, she at last threw herself against his
neck and pleaded with him to drink, liberally sprinkling
her murmurs with endearments and losing herself so much
in her concern for the foal that she jumped violently when a
man's voice came from the half door behind her.

'If you used just a few of those terms to a man, he'd
have you wedded and bedded in no time!'

Her eyes, tears trembling on the edge, abstractedly took
in Ben's transformed appearance. He had showered
recently, his hair still darkened by the water, and the grime
had disappeared from his face and torso, which was only
partially covered by an unbuttoned shirt.

'Ben, he won't eat!' she cried despairingly, ignoring his
comment and not questioning her heady sense of relief when
he joined her in the stall and refastened the door. 'He hasn't
had anything since Phil fed him early this morning.'

Ben stood frowning thoughtfully down at the small
animal, then crouched beside Abby so that his arm brushed
hers as he stretched out a hand to fondle the nervously
twitching ears. His voice was soothing in its caressing
murmur although he used none of the more flowery endearments Abby had employed. She, like the colt, became
mesmerised by the gentleness in his man's voice and her
thoughts veered away from the stable to a scene in her
mind's eye where Ben was making love to a faceless woman.
What words would he murmur then in the heat of passion?
When those well formed muscular arms, with their dusting
of bronze hairs, held the woman he loved?

Colour swept instantly into her face when her eyes came
round to meet his and she realised he had been calling her
name softly. A gleam of amused mockery flashed into the

narrowed green of his as if, again, he knew exactly where her thoughts had been, but all he said was: 'The milk—I'll try him again.'

Confused, she turned quickly and extracted the bottle from the bucket, handing it to him and watching while he smeared some of the milk on the middle finger of his left hand and pushed it between the velvety lips. As soon as the foal started to suck vigorously, Ben inserted the nipple of the bottle and gradually withdrew his finger until it was free.

'I tried that!' Abby said indignantly.

'Maybe your fingers aren't the right size,' Ben remarked casually. 'That's my boy,' he said more enthusiastically, and glanced up at Abby. 'Like most babies, he prefers the real thing.'

Pink flooded back to Abby's neck and face and she pulled herself back on to the piled straw away from him, hitching up her knees and hooking her arms round them. 'Some mothers bring their babies up entirely on bottles, and they——'

'The mother of my children won't,' he interrupted brusquely, returning his attention to the diminishing level of milk in the bottle. 'Doing things the way nature intended is always the best way.'

Embarrassment made Abby's tone sharp as she retorted: 'And suppose your—your wife doesn't want to ...'

Ben dropped from a crouch to his knees before answering. 'The woman I marry will want to because she'll know it's as natural as what went before.'

If Abby had been warm with embarrassment at his previous words, it was nothing to the crimson heat that now spread like a forest fire over her entire body and left even her toes tingling. No man had ever been as forthrightly explicit in her presence as Ben was now being, and he seemed surprised by the red glow in her cheeks that made her eyes sparkle with deeper blue. The foal was already on the point of dozing when he withdrew the empty container, and to Abby's surprise he came to sit beside her on the piled straw and lifted her face to his.

'For a ranch girl you're surprisingly modest about certain basic facts, aren't you? Have you led that sheltered a life?'

Abby jerked her chin away. What did he mean by 'modest'? That she was a shrinking violet because she didn't care to discuss what he called 'basic facts' with Ben Franklin?

'Just because I don't care to talk about—basic facts—with any stranger who happens along——'

'Stranger? Come on, Abby, I'm hardly a stranger ... in fact, I've probably been closer to you than anybody ever has been. And I don't think I'm wrong when I say that you liked being that close to me, or that you should change your thinking about marriage.'

Abby struggled to rise to her feet, but found his arm like a steel band round her waist holding her back. Furiously, she turned to wither him with the words springing to her lips, but her forehead brushed against the slight abrassiveness of his chin and she had to swallow before she spoke.

'You have the biggest head of any man I ever knew, Ben Franklin! Because I let you kiss me a couple of times you think you've groomed me for stardom in some overbearing man's life! Well, thanks, but no, thanks! I can live very happily without kisses from you or any other man.'

'Can you?' he asked with meaningful huskiness, his breath fanning her mouth warmly. 'That wasn't the impression I got the four—not two—times I kissed you.'

'So? You're better at arithmetic than I am,' she snapped, turning her head away from the disturbing breath on her lips only to find that on her ear it gave an even more distracting sensation. More galling were his soft-toned chuckle and his hand cupping her resistless chin to bring it round to him.

The green eyes were warm as they smiled half mockingly, half seriously into hers. 'You're not a very good liar, Abby. There's a little pulse at your throat that tells me you'd like me to kiss you again right now, and I doubt if I'd be far out in saying that your heart's beating just as fast as that little pulse.' As he spoke, his sun-bronzed hand came up to lie against the telltale anxious thud at her breast.

'Of course it would,' she struggled for control and pushed

his hand away. 'One's connected to the other in case you didn't know, and don't let it swell your head even more. Anger makes the heart pump faster too, you know!'

'Is that what it is?' he drawled lazily, only the rustle of straw beneath her head making her aware that he had slickly manoeuvred her on to her back. His head was outlined in burnished copper in the small square of light from the half door, his lean face shadowed as it bent over hers, and she licked lips that were suddenly dry as her darkened eyes stared up to the obscured narrowness of his.

'I don't think so, Abby ... weren't you thinking of being kissed just a little while ago? You were so lost in your daydream you didn't even hear me speak to you. You want me to kiss you right now, don't you?' he urged softly, his head bending just a shade closer to hers.

'No!—no!' She felt the sharp prick of dried straw beneath her head as she moved it from side to side. 'Let me up, Ben!'

'Not until you tell me the truth, Abby. You want me to kiss you, don't you?' he persisted, his mouth poised a breath away from the lips she compressed with effort.

'No!'

'Yes! Like this, and this, and this ...' His lips touched and lifted tantalisingly from hers while his hands went with deliberate intent over the soft rise of her breast under her blue plaid shirt. Her own hands came up to push against the hard wall of his chest, but stayed there inert on the curling wiriness of short hairs that did nothing to hide the quickening hammer of his heart against her palms. 'Say yes, Abby,' he whispered then at her ear. 'Tell me you want me to kiss you.'

Her lips shaped a denial, but the combined effect of his caressing hands and warm breath on her ear brought instead an explosive: 'Yes! ... yes,' then a sigh that spoke more of dying than living. The gleam—of triumph? desire? —in the opaque green of his eyes was visible for only a fleeting moment before individual features were blotted out and nothing existed except his warm breath filling her mouth, his lips not harshly demanding as they had been before, but gently, sensuously probing in a way that sent heat like molten lava down through her body and left her weak. Her arms slid round under his shirt to clutch convulsively round his waist and draw his weight further down on her.

Under her fingers the sun-baked warmth of his back undulated over smoothly co-ordinated muscles which had no trace of superfluous flesh on them ... the hardness was all male, and sent that message from her fingertips to the feminine centre of her being, the core that similarly made her melting submission to his masculinity potently clear to him.

His mouth moved from hers to the quivering sensitivity of her ear, murmuring there all the endearments she had imagined a short time ago, and all the time his hands were being used as well-experienced instruments of arousal. Abby was drowning in a sea of diffused sensation, and at the same time she was crossing the plateau of her previous vision where now the mountain at the end of it was no more than an easily climbed hill. When Ben's lips returned with heightened urgency to her mouth, his whole body express-ing unchecked desire, Abby yielded and returned his passion with an abandon that sent shock waves washing over her and left her with only the mindless need to merge with this man, to be one with him, the missing half of his vital force. But ...

'No, Ben! No,' she moaned against the mouth she pushed away with a strength she dredged from some unknown source. This wasn't the time to climb that mountain. It was too soon ... there were too many untied ends flapping aim-lessly in her mind ...

'Abby?' Ben's head was outlined once more against the patch of sky outside, and even though his face was shadowed, Abby saw that his colour had paled under the tan. His eyes gleamed narrowly under half-closed lids—eyes that swept from the deepened violet blue of hers to her hair and back to the tremulous curve of her mouth. It was then, as she watched, that she saw his gradual withdrawal in the firming of his jaw, the caution returning to his eyes, and oddly felt his physical removal although his body was still pressed in a close line to hers. 'Abby, I——'

'Don't worry, Ben,' her breath caught through the hurt

that seared her. 'You don't have to marry me because you kissed me that way.'

The straw crackled under him as he moved suddenly and sat up a body width away from her. One hand clasped tightly round his chin, his elbow supported on the knee he had drawn up, his fingers moved several times on his jaw before he said without looking at her:

'I can't ask you to marry me, Abby ... not now.'

'Have I ever said I wanted you to?' she threw back, getting to her feet and glaring down at him until he unwound his length from the floor and regarded her with an intent kind of sadness.

'No,' he agreed quietly, 'you never have. But I think you know as well as I do that there's something between us that has to be settled one way or the other. Either by marriage or ...'

'Or by running away from me as you did from Sylvia?' she tilted her chin to say scathingly before twirling on her heel and going to the door without a backward glance at him or the sleeping foal. She made no attempt to re-close the half door, but went straight to the house and along to her bedroom to throw herself across the bed, burying her face in the pillows. Determined not to cry, she vented her emotions by cursing in turn Ben Franklin, who had turned her life around so that it would never be the same again, and Sylvia, who had bound him even more closely than the legal bonds that tied her to her husband.

The afternoon was hot, and not many people occupied the main street when Abby drove along it to reach the lumber yard. Curt Hansen, the stocky tow-haired son of the owner, looked at her across the counter in the store part of the yard, compassion in the light blue of his eyes.

'Sorry to hear about what happened, Abby. It was a lucky thing the whole place didn't catch fire. Who would have thought Dave Corben would be crazy enough to do something like that? Have they caught him yet?'

'I believe so,' Abby said shortly, taking Ben's list from her pocket and placing it flat on the counter. 'The new man

I've got in place of Dave wants this stuff as soon as you can get it out to the ranch.'

Sensing her unwillingness to talk about the tragedy, Curt scanned Ben's clear, unornamented script with eyes that were already knowledgeable in spite of his youth. 'Is he a builder, this new man of yours?' he asked at last, blond eyebrows rising in surprise.

'No—why?'

'Everything's down here to the last nail he'll need. He must know something about construction.'

'Maybe,' Abby shrugged. 'All I'm interested in is how good he is at being a ranch foreman, and he's been okay that way so far.'

Curt's eyes went back cursorily down the list. 'Well, I think we have everything in stock that he needs—we can get it out to Cedar Hills first thing tomorrow if we load it up this afternoon.'

'Thanks, Curt.'

Five minutes later Abby had parked the car on the main street and was walking past Verna's exclusive dress shop when Debby rushed out.

'Abby! I was coming out to see you tonight. Believe it or not, I didn't hear about the fire till this morning ...' She chattered on in her animated way about the perfidy of Dave and Wally, evidently having received an exaggerated account of their criminal activities, which now seemingly included every small robbery the small town had known in recent years. In the end, weary of even thinking about Dave and the loss of Glory, Abby interposed and said she had several more things to do while she was in town.

'Haven't you time to come in and see some of Verna's bargains?' her friend said, taking amiably to the change of subject. 'She's selling everything way below cost because she's closing permanently at the end of next week when she goes back to Vancouver.'

'No, thanks,' Abby returned with a wry smile, remembering the one dress she had bought from there which had been successful in everyone else's eyes except Ben's. 'I really have to go, Debby. See you soon.'

For the first time in her memory, Abby was glad to get

away from her friend's exuberant company. Debby was too bubbly, too overwhelmingly in love with the man she was going to marry, to be the confidante she had been in former times. Abby knew, and shuddered at the thought, that Debby would be appropriately sympathetic in knowing that her lifelong friend was hopelessly in love with a man who found her attractive enough to kiss with devastating passion yet who held back any deeper commitment because he loved a woman who could never belong to him.

In the small post office, where she collected the ranch mail, the garrulous woman clerk said: 'There's one for your new man, too—he usually comes in and picks up his own, but as you're in town it won't do any harm to let you take it for him.'

Reaching behind her, the older woman produced a letter addressed in a bold yet feminine handwriting, and Abby stacked it on top of the other mail, which was mostly in the form of circulars and the never ending bills for various ranch expenses.

All the way back to Cedar Hills the letter for Ben lay beside Abby on the front seat, the flamboyant writing etching itself deeper on her consciousness each time she looked at it. Instinct, prompted by the kind of jealousy she had never known before, told her it was from Sylvia, and in her mind's eye she conjured up a picture of a vibrantly attractive woman, freely assertive yet with an aura of all-out femininity which Ben would admire. Why couldn't she be content with his brother, whose wife she was? If she loved Ben at all, wouldn't she make at least some effort to respect his sacrifice in staying away from her and the rest of his family? But here she was writing to him, keeping alive the flame even if it was only through the cold medium of letters.

At the ranch, Abby gave Harry a letter from her daughter-in-law in Kamloops and took the rest of the mail to the office, fingering the one addressed to Ben for a long time before grasping it more firmly and going to the bungalow to deliver it.

Ben was in the kitchen frying something on the stove when she knocked at his door, and he called: 'Come in, Abby,' when he looked round in answer to her summons.

Hesitating for only a moment, Abby pulled open the screen door and marched briskly to the table. 'There's a letter for you. It's addressed to your post office box, but Ida Garrison thought I might as well bring it with the rest of the mail.' How many other letters had come from Sylvia addressed to the anonymity of a post office box?

Ben came towards her wiping his hands on a tea-towel, his eyes uncommunicatively shuttered as they went from the letter on the table to Abby's cool expression.

'Thanks. I took a post office box because I didn't want you to be bothered with my personal mail, but it seems Mrs Garrison thinks otherwise.' His eyes looked directly into hers as he went on blandly: 'Did you take the list in to the lumber yard?'

'Of course. The order will be here first thing tomorrow.'

He seemed pleased, and more at ease than Abby would have thought possible after the recent scene in the stable. 'Good girl! I knew those blue eyes would charm a monkey off a tree.'

'Charm had nothing to do with it,' Abby retorted, turning on her heel and going to the door. 'Carl was more impressed with your detailed list than with the colour of my eyes.' Her head swivelled round to look back at him. 'I'll leave you in peace to read your letter.'

'It can wait till I've finished cooking my supper,' he said casually. 'But thanks for bringing it.'

The aroma of the steak he was frying followed her to the house, and she fought down the surge of pity that threatened to engulf her. It wasn't her business that Ben Franklin was cooking for himself and would eat his meal completely on his own ... if it was anyone's concern, it was Sylvia's, who seemingly wanted to hunt with the hounds and run with the hare. Why should Abby Mackenzie feel guilty because a man was cooking for and eating by himself?

CHAPTER ELEVEN

It was after the coffee break the next morning, when the new lumber was stacked neatly beside the now cleared barn site, that Ben said:

'Abby, would you mind going over to my place and getting my tape measure? I think you'll find it in the living room, I was using it last night. The old barn was a few inches out here and there, but I'd like this one to be dead right.'

Prompted to tell him to find it himself, Abby stifled the words when her eyes went once again over his dirt-smeared skin and the tired grooves beside his mouth. It was early in the day, but maybe he hadn't slept too well—had Sylvia said something to upset him in her letter?

Turning away without a word, she crossed to the bungalow and scanned every surface in the living room in hopes of not having to venture further, but there was no sign of the tape he needed. He was a tidy man, she conceded, glancing at the clear counter tops and scoured sink in the kitchen, but the item she sought wasn't there either. In the bedroom, the double bed was still unmade from Ben's obviously restless sleep of the night before, and without thinking Abby moved across to it and straightened the tousled sheets and blankets, leaving it as neat as she always did her own bed in the main house before turning to look round for the tape.

It was there on the dressing table, and her hand had closed round it when her eye fell on the open letter beside it. The envelope she had brought from town lay a little distance from the pale blue notepaper, so there was no doubt that the letter was the one she had delivered to Ben yesterday. Although she hadn't intended to read it, the words leapt out to Abby's stricken eyes.

'Ben darling,' the flowing script read, 'I hope you can get away for a few days the week after next to come down to Kamloops. There's a sale of Hereford bulls there, and it goes without saying that your dad and George want to be where that action is. Again, it goes without saying that I'll be there too. It seems such ages since you were here, dearest Ben, and I can't say how wonderful it will be to see you again, so please try to make it. Maybe I can entice you down to Kamloops by saying that I have some exciting news for you . . .'

What Sylvia was using as enticement to get Ben to Kamloops was a closed book to Abby, because the first page ended there and she was too filled with guilt at reading that far to turn over to the second . . . but if she was using the news as enticement, Ben wouldn't know either. What could it be? Had Sylvia at last told her husband about her relationship with Ben, so that now she was free to come to him? Abby moved frozenly away from the bedroom, but the clear-cut strokes of Sylvia's writing were vivid in her brain when she hurried back into the sunshine again.

Ben nodded an abstracted thanks when she handed the tape measure to him and turned immediately to Tom Edwards, Clint's father, to resume their discussion. Feeling rebuffed, she turned away and made for Beau's stall. Since Ben's session with him the day before, the young horse had taken gladly to the nourishment offered him, and Abby's mind wandered as the animal sucked vigorously enough to send the level of milk down rapidly.

Fancying that the straw where she had lain with Ben yesterday still held the imprint of their bodies, she averted her eyes from it. Would he have kissed her that way if he had known the love of his life was to be so near in such a little while? And had he, like Abby, guessed the reason why Sylvia was anxious to see him in Kamloops?

A prickling sensation at the back of her eyes presaged the storm of self-pity, the dissipated confidence that tore through her. Ben had made it more than clear that, compared to Sylvia—and secondarily Verna—Abby was a poor excuse for a woman in his eyes. A girl who struck him as

being 'provocative' in the jeans she wore most of the time
was no more than a source of amusement to him. Masculine
amusement . . . the kind that drew no reverential adoration
for a beloved woman, however many times he made love to
her in a stable with the smells and sounds of the ranch
around them . . . All he had wanted to do was to prove that
his male power could overcome even Abby Mackenzie's
scruples. Her skin itched with the knowledge of how well
he had done just that.

That day he made no appearance in the stable, seeming
still absorbed in his measurements of the new barn when
Abby passed some time later. It wasn't until the next day
that she found herself partially isolated with him at the
coffee break that he spoke to her without the foreman-
to-boss politeness he used in front of the neighbouring
ranchers.

'Thanks for making my bed yesterday,' he said with only
a faint gleam of amusement behind his light green eyes. 'It
made me feel as if I had a wife who cared—except that I
had to sleep all alone, and that took the bloom off it considerably.'

In spite of her efforts at control, Abby's face glowed
hotly as she glanced up at him and away again. Her fingers
tightened round the coffee mug she held.

'I'd have thought you'd be used to the idea of sleeping
alone for the rest of your life—or your brother's,' she said
crushingly, feeling a savage stab of satisfaction when he
stiffened beside her.

'What's that supposed to mean?'

Her attempt at a light laugh fell somewhat flat. 'Isn't it
obvious? You don't believe in divorce, so it doesn't need
a genius to work out that you'll have to wait a long time to
take your brother's place in Sylvia's bed!'

There was something frightening about the loud indrawn
hiss of his breath, the instant leaching of colour from the
skin surrounding his eyes. Abby wanted to get up and run,
but found herself glued to the stack of new wood where
they sat. Fear made her voice defensive when she went on:

'Or are you hoping she'll have much better news for you
when you get to Kamloops?'

'Oh, I see,' he said, his voice ominously controlled to evenness. 'I should have known you couldn't resist a letter any more than a phone call you listened in to. You read Sylvia's letter when you went to get the tape for me, didn't you?' Contempt lashed from his eyes.

'No!' she cried indignantly, then subsided on her perch when honesty compelled her to admit: 'Only the first page —and I couldn't help seeing that, you'd left it out for anyone in the world to look at!'

'In my bedroom? One of these days, Abby,' he told her grimly, 'I'm going to take you over my knee and beat some sense into you. A sense of what's right and wrong, and how far you can try a man before he wrings your soft little neck!' There was little of invitation in his next words. 'I want you to come with me to Kamloops and meet Sylvia and my brother and father. Then you might understand a lot of things that haven't made sense to that addled brain of yours.'

'I do not have an addled brain,' she threw back frostily. 'If anyone has it's you, Ben Franklin! The cows have to be moved up to summer pasture, so there's no way you, or I, can go to Kamloops the week after next.' She flushed pink, knowing she had quoted Sylvia's sentence word for word, and Ben's level stare told her that he hadn't missed that fact either.

'The barn should be finished in three more days at most, with the help we have now and the others who have promised to come,' he reminded her coldly. 'It shouldn't take more than a week to drive the cattle up to summer pasture, so we'll have plenty of time to get down to Kamloops for the sale.'

'If you think I'm going to rush back from a cattle drive——'

'No, you won't be doing that,' he interrupted tersely, rising and looking down at her tight-lipped. 'For the very good reason that you won't be going on the cattle drive.'

'Not——?' Abby glared belligerently up at him and jumped off the wood pile, finding her advantage not much greater as her head still had to be tilted to look into his glittering green eyes. 'I *always* go on the cattle drive!'

'This time you're going to stay home where you belong,' he threw down into her spluttering disbelief. 'There are more important things a woman can do at home instead of trying to be one of the boys!'

'I could do some tatting or hook a rug,' she jeered.

'If that's what takes your fancy,' he shrugged maddeningly. 'Or you can tend to the motherless foal who looks to you for affection and care. I don't give a damn what you do, Abby,' he moved off with a contemptuous toss of his shoulders, 'as long as it's not coming on a cattle drive.'

Abby stemmed the hot reply that rose to her lips, because to reach Ben's ears she would have had to shout and the other men would hear her too. Fuming inwardly, she stamped off to the office, throwing herself in the desk chair and contemplating the ceiling with moodily furrowed brow. How dare Ben Franklin dictate to her, Abby Mackenzie, what she would or wouldn't do? As if he had the right to walk into Cedar Hills a stranger and take over as if the place belonged to him!

Some time later, when Harry asked her about re-stocking the freezer with meat before the herd was moved up north, she snapped: 'Why ask me? You'd better ask Ben Franklin —he seems to have taken over here.'

Harry lifted her brows and looked in astonishment after the indignant motion of Abby's hips as she walked away, then shook her head in puzzlement though a thoughtful gleam lit her eyes.

Work proceeded apace on the barn and, with many hands to help, the new structure was in position by the weekend. The replacement barn was similar in outer contours to the old one, but Ben had incorporated more modern ideas for the interior design which drew the admiration of several ranchers who had helped in the restoration, one of them going so far as to say he wouldn't mind his own barn burning down if Ben would design him a new one.

Conversation between Abby and Ben had been limited to polite exchanges in front of the others, and if they sensed a coolness on her part the men overlooked it in their new-found admiration of Ben's capabilities.

'If you ever need a job, Ben,' Tom Edwards said half jokingly, 'you know where to come.' Still smiling, he turned to Abby. 'You've a good man here, Abby—don't let him slip through your fingers.'

Abby's eyes flashed blue lights of contempt in Ben's direction as she replied shortly: 'I might have no choice about that. Our Mr Franklin has a she-devil inside him that drives him on from place to place without letting him settle anywhere for long!' Not waiting to see more than Ben's quick jerk of the head and narrowed eyes on her face, she turned on her heel and left a surprised-looking Tom to whatever explanation Ben cared to give him.

But the foreman had no intention of letting her get away with the barbed remark, cornering her later as she was passing his bungalow on her way back to the house for supper. His eyes held the cool incommunicative green of a cat's as he leaned across her and opened the screen door so that she had no option but to step inside. Two paces and she turned to face him, defiant hands on her slim hips.

'What do you want?' she asked in a clipped voice. 'I'm busy.'

'I want to know what you meant by that crack to Tom Edwards! The only devil I can think of in my life right now is you, but you obviously didn't mean yourself.' Anger glinted behind the narrow slits of his lids. 'Though I'd be the first to admit that if anybody could drive a man away it would be you.'

Abby took a deep breath and her nostrils flared dangerously. 'Then why don't you go? Did I ask you to come here?—do you see me on my knees begging you to stay?'

He sighed in exasperation. 'No, but then you'd never do that even if——' Breaking off abruptly, he did a swift about turn and went to the table where his cigars lay, lighting one and sending up a cloud of smoke before looking at her again. 'I'll leave, if that's what you want, as soon as we get back from Kamloops.'

'That's a joke,' she jeered. 'If it's what I want? You know darned well it's likely what *you'll* want after you see your dear, sweet Sylvia again!'

Ben's expression was hard to see behind the smoke-screen curling up from the cigar, and when her view cleared there was just a hard-jawed blandness in the look he gave her.

'Maybe,' he agreed quietly. 'That depends on you.'

'On me? What am I supposed to do?—keep your big brother occupied while you make up for lost time with his wife?'

It seemed she had no sooner heard the sharp intake of his breath when he had thrown his cigar into the ashtray and reached her in two strides, picking her up under one arm and carrying her struggling figure over to a high-backed chair where he sat down and bent her over his knees.

'Don't you dare, Ben Franklin!' she squealed, and saw his hand lift. 'I'm warning you—*oh*!'

The pain of his well-aimed slaps was nothing compared to the injury to her dignity as she struggled impotently against the steel band of his arm holding her across his knees. When at last he released her and stood her on her feet, the tears sparkling in her eyes were composed of molten fury.

'You'll regret that,' she breathed, fire licking her tongue, her breast rising and falling rapidly under the thinness of her shirt. 'To begin with, you can get off this ranch and never come within fifty miles of it again!' She reached the door, her feet scarcely touching the floor, and turned back to throw at him:

'I can organise a cattle drive without *your* help, Ben Franklin!'

Again he had moved up beside her in an instant, his mouth showing white round its edges as he grasped the wrist she had raised to open the door.

'You're not organising any cattle drive,' he told her harshly, 'and you're coming to Kamloops with me if I have to hog-tie you and drag you there.'

'All brute force, aren't you?' she sneered, letting her wrist lie loose against his palm.

'I'm sorry if I hurt you,' he apologised stiffly, 'but it's something you've been asking for and I make no apology for doing it.' He let her wrist go. 'I'll be away with the cows for the next week, so you won't be bothered with my company. As soon as I get back, we'll take off for Kamloops. After that, it's up to you whether I go or stay.'

Angry words trembled on the edge of her lips before she compressed them and gave a faint shrug, contenting herself with a venomous look over her shoulder at him as she went out and let the door slam behind her. What was the use of arguing with a man who would go right ahead and do what he wanted anyway? A man who proved himself superior, he thought, by using brute force against a girl less than half his size! For sheer male arrogance, he could beat her father and the Wests hands down, but she had no intention of giving in meekly to his high-handed tactics. If necessary, she would get that kindly-eyed Sergeant Mathers to put Ben Franklin off the ranch and out of her life for ever.

But Abby put off her plans for evicting Ben, and then it was too late because, after bidding her a coolly polite farewell, he had taken off with most of the men for the tedious drive north to greener pastures.

Although her own chores were doubled and tripled because of the men's absence, the days hung heavy on Abby's hands and the unnatural quietness around the buildings made her snappish even with Harry. Phil had gone to round out the numbers needed for the drive, so the two women ate alone in the dinette in the kitchen. On the third night, Abby dropped on to the bench seat and sighed when Harry came to sit opposite and started her meal.

'What's wrong, honey?' she enquired, looking concernedly into the stormy blue eyes across the table.

'It's so dead with everybody away!' Abby burst out, picking up her fork but only pushing the food round furiously on her plate. 'I should have insisted on going on the drive instead of letting Ben Franklin dictate what I would do.'

Harry smiled with serene complacency. 'I miss Phil too, but just think how nice it's going to be when they come back.'

'I didn't say I miss *Ben*!' snapped Abby.

'I know you didn't, but that's what you meant, isn't it? When you love somebody, every day seems a year when they're not there.'

'I didn't say that either!' Abby glared.

'You didn't have to,' the older woman returned equably, lifting her fork to her mouth and going on after a few moments: 'You've been in love with him for quite some time, haven't you?'

'I certainly have not! He's the most arrogant, overbearing man I've ever met in my life! He's a prime example of what I've always hated about men, and ...' her eyes filled suddenly with tears and she ended on a wail, '—I *love* him, H-Harry!'

In a second the housekeeper was on her feet, and in another she was pressing the red-gold head to her ample bosom as she had untold times in the past with the motherless girl in her charge. 'There now,' she soothed, 'and what's that to cry about? It's the happiest time in a girl's life when she falls in love with the right man.'

'But he's not the right man!' Abby cried, pulling away from the comforting bosom and fumbling in her pocket for a tissue, which she rubbed fiercely across her eyes. Harry went thoughtfully back to her own seat. 'He—he's in love with s-somebody else, and he always w-will be!'

Before she could stop the halting words, Abby told Harry about Ben's sister-in-law, the one he had admitted to loving.

'*Ben's* in love with his brother's wife?' Harry echoed, startled. 'He told you that?'

Abby nodded. 'He said he l-loved her, but that I—I wouldn't understand. He admires her—she's everything I'm not.' A dark frown pulled down her brows. 'She calls him "Ben darling" and wants him to go to Kamloops next week when she's there with her husband and Ben's father. I can't imagine why he wants me to go down there with him, but——'

Harry looked at her sharply. 'He wants you to go? Why would he want that?'

'How should I know?' Abby shrugged impatiently. 'Maybe so that his father and brother won't suspect anything if he takes another girl with him.'

The housekeeper shook her head decisively. 'No, that doesn't sound like the Ben I know. He would be as honest in those things as my Phil.' She looked appraisingly at Abby's tousled hair and tear-stained eyes, lengthening her gaze to take in the plain blue cotton shirt that showed above the table. 'You know, Abby, if I was in love with a man like Ben, I sure as heck wouldn't hand him over on a platter to a woman who already has a husband. I'd fight like a tiger for him.'

'Oh, Harry!' Abby smiled through her tears, her imagination trying and failing to come up with a picture of the plump Harry doing battle with a woman who had every quality a man like Ben admired. 'What do you suggest I should do? Go down there and challenge her to a pitchfork battle?'

'No. Meet her on her own ground. Like most men, Ben likes women to be pretty and feminine at least some of the time. Go to the sale Verna's having at her store and fit yourself out with clothes that make you look like a female a man's proud to be seen with.' More severely, Harry added: 'But just wearing pretty clothes isn't the whole of it by a long way, Abby. No man likes a woman who tries to be his equal in every blessed thing; it's part of his manliness to want to take care of the woman he loves, to feel that she depends on him to do whatever he does best in the same way he depends on her for what only she can supply. The only equality there can be between a man and a woman is that they love each other equally.'

The blue eyes that had been fixed on the older woman's face refilled with tears and dropped to stare sightlessly at the untouched food. 'I do love him that way,' Abby whispered, 'but——'

'He's kissed you, hasn't he? More than once, I'd guess.'

Abby flushed, her tears stopping as anger flickered at her nerve ends again. 'He's also spanked me!' she flared without thinking, and looked up in amazed indignation at Harry's hearty chuckle. 'You think that's funny?'

'No, but I think it's a very good sign. Unless he's one of those sick men who go around beating women up— which Ben is not!—a man doesn't spank a girl unless he feels responsible for her. Come on, now,' Harry's twinkling smile faded, 'eat your supper or I'll have to re-heat it.'

Sniffing, but somehow not feeling as bad as she had before, Abby did so.

CHAPTER TWELVE

IF Ben noticed the new oatmeal-coloured pants suit Abby was wearing when he came to pick her up the following Sunday, there was only a faint flicker in his narrowed eyes to prove it. He had told her to bring enough clothing for a stay of several days, and again, if he was surprised at the weight of the suitcase she had packed with several outfits bought from Verna's store, there was no sign of it. His only smile was the farewell one he gave Harry, and Abby felt uncomfortable as he drove down the long driveway and turned on to the highway.

Fingering the slender golden chain belt surrounding her waist, she wondered why he had insisted on bringing her when he was making it so obvious that he didn't want her there.

It had been late the afternoon before when he and the other men got home from the drive, and she had put down his coolly remote manner to his obvious tiredness. Like a good foreman, he had come to the house to give a report, but had politely refused Harry's invitation to stay for supper.

But it wasn't tiredness that made him uncommunicative now, Abby thought, giving him a sideways glance. The deepened facial lines of yesterday were erased to their normal scarcely noticeable appearance, his eyes calmly alert as they faced the road ahead. No one in the world had such cold-looking eyes as Ben did at times, yet when he had kissed her they had held the torrid heat of a tropic sea. She turned her head away when her eyes reached the determined jut of his lean jaw.

'Shouldn't we have made reservations?' she asked, her voice low. Anything to break the uncompanionable silence,

167

though it seemed not to bother him.

'That's been taken care of,' he replied briefly without taking his eyes from the road, though he did spare a momentary glance at her averted profile when she gave a faint sigh. 'I like what you're wearing—is it new?'

'Yes.' She made no attempt to turn her head and meet his eyes. 'I didn't think you'd want me to meet your family in jeans and shirt.' She had been going to say 'meet Sylvia', but thought better of it.

'They'll be very impressed,' was all he said, and turned on the radio, twisting the dial until the car was filled with soft music ... as if he didn't want the effort of making conversation, she thought, but it no longer bothered her and she leaned back against the seat and closed her eyes.

The music must have lulled her to sleep, because they were entering Kamloops when Ben spoke her name softly. 'Abby? We're just about there.'

Startled, she sat up and saw the bare grass hills surrounding the city which was set in the middle of ranching country. Small, neatly kept houses with well tended gardens slid past on either hand, and then Ben was turning off on a side street. His brow furrowed as he looked for the hotel they were to stay at, and his jaw seemed more tightly clenched than ever. Tension at the thought of seeing Sylvia again? Abby wondered sourly.

The hotel was a six-storey sweep of white set back from the road, wrought iron balconies giving a warm Spanish touch. Abby had never stayed there before, and her eyes widened in awe as Ben took her elbow to lead her through the impressive entrance.

'Is your family staying here too?' she gave him an upward glance that held more of speculation than question. He had never spoken about his family's circumstances, or even told her where they lived apart from a laconic 'South.' But their choice of a place to stay on their cattle-buying trip would be an indication that they were far from scraping a bare living from their land.

Ben nodded, still tight-lipped and somehow distracted. 'Dad stayed here with my mother once when I was young, so I guessed he wouldn't go anywhere else in Kamloops.'

Leading her to a deeply sunk armchair beside a large potted plant inside the door, he told her to wait there while he went back for their luggage. 'We'll get settled in our rooms before we find the others.'

He was unlike the Ben she had come to know in so many different ways, and this aspect of him was one she didn't care for at all, but she forgot the sinking feeling she had about him as she watched the comings and goings in the spacious lobby. That many of the guests were ranch people here for the sale was obvious in their dress and the way the men walked with casual forcefulness across the patterned carpet, which deadened the sound their leather boots would have made on a tiled floor. Ben, in his tan short jacket and beige pants, would blend into them with no trouble at all.

At that moment he came back through the glass doors and she amended her last thought. Even among others of his kind, Ben would stand out as a man on his own, a man she would pick out instantly in a crowd of a thousand, a man she loved as she had never thought to love any member of the male species. It didn't matter that his heart belonged to another woman; he was the only one whose touch set up in Abby the quivering desire for more, to know him in the ultimate way a man and woman knew each other.

He indicated with a nod that she should stay where she was until he had checked in, and her eyes never left his broad-shouldered, lean-hipped figure as he crossed to the reception desk, dropping their bags close to his feet. The dark-haired clerk he spoke to evidently wasn't blind to his attractions either as she smiled beguilingly up into his face and handed him the keys to the rooms. The smile disappeared abruptly from her face, however, when Ben turned away from the counter and another woman shouted 'Ben!' and rushed towards him from the far side of the hall.

Ben's arms opened to greet the tallish tow-haired woman who ran to throw her arms round him in delight, her gurgling pleasure at being lifted up and twirled round several times by Ben audible even to Abby in her remote corner. Jealousy surged like adrenalin through her veins and had a similar effect on her reflexes, which tensed her muscles preparatory to fleeing from the sight of two people so happy to see each other that they cared nothing for the curious smiles directed at them.

At least they could have made their joyful reunion less public, she thought bitterly, seeing as she did that although they had stopped kissing each other, Ben's arms were still firmly round the other woman's waist while he looked down at her with eyes crinkled in a smile such as he had never given herself. If he'd had a tail, she told herself waspishly, it would have been wagging a mile a minute at that moment.

Her impetus to flee only got her as far as her feet before she saw that Ben, his arm still round that shapely waist, was leading Sylvia over to her corner. A hurried look on Abby's part left her with a sharp feeling of wonder that Ben should choose this woman above all others to be the recipient of his devotion. Much taller than Abby, her fair-skinned face bore clear evidence of long hours spent under a hot sun, light freckles joining together across her nose and cheeks to give a tanned appearance. A pale blue pants suit, the colour of her eyes, emphasised the long slender torso and length of leg.

And then Sylvia smiled as Ben introduced them, and Abby no longer wondered at Ben's devotion. That wide, encompassing smile did more than hint at an underlying sense of humour and understanding for all the follies of human nature, and was the one redeeming feature which would captivate any man and make him hers for ever. Even Abby felt the tug of it, and her answering smile was far less forced than she would have thought possible a few minutes before.

'It's wonderful to meet you at long last,' Sylvia said, a slight frown coming between her brows when she glanced up at Ben's face and saw the deeper frown there. 'I mean,' she turned back to Abby, 'Ben's written so much about you since he's been at Cedar Hills.'

It was Abby's turn to look at Ben now, but he returned her gaze with bland unconcern. 'Thank you,' she said to Sylvia. 'I've—heard quite a bit about you, too—about all of you.'

The other woman seemed surprised by this. 'Have you? I

didn't think Ben would have said much about—his family.'

'Oh, yes,' Abby said airily, enjoying Ben's sudden discomfort. 'I know quite a lot about you.'

'Well, we can go into all this later,' Ben interposed coolly. 'We'll see where our rooms are, Sylvia, then I'll bring Abby along to Dad's room. What number is it?'

Sylvia laughed indulgently. 'You know what Dad's like! He's taken a suite with a sitting room so that we can talk in privacy.' Her voice sobered. 'He's missed you, Ben. We all have, and he can't wait to see you again so don't take too long. He's in 425—and I'll have to go now and find out if the hotel shop has his favourite brand of cigars, or he'll be fit to be tied.'

Ben smiled as if remembering well his parent's wrath when roused, and followed Sylvia a few steps to murmur softly with bent head to her ear. Whatever the words were they were sufficient to bring Sylvia's eyes back with a worried frown to glance off Abby, then back to Ben with a shake of her head. Was Sylvia complaining about him bringing another girl when she had expected to have him to herself for these few days? More words from Ben, and he seemed satisfied when she smiled, nodding, and squeezed his arm. Abby, humiliated, wondered if the other girl's restored good humour was because Ben had arranged a private meeting later, and something of this thought showed in her mutinously pursed lips when Ben turned back to her.

'What's the matter?' he asked quietly as they walked together to the desk where he picked up their bags and led her to the elevators at the far side of the lobby. 'Didn't you like Sylvia?'

'Does it matter whether I like her or not?' she retorted with asperity. 'I'm sure she's only interested in your feelings, and you made them abundantly clear for all to see when you met her!'

'You sound like a jealous woman,' he smiled enigmatically, and leaned casually against the elevator wall as it bore them up to the sixth floor. His voice took on an edge of seriousness. 'You might hate me for other things, Abby, but don't on Sylvia's account. She's very happy with my brother.'

'Until you came on the scene!' She stepped out ahead of
him to the carpeted passage and followed him to a room
halfway along on their right, knowing that he would gladly
have turned her across his knee again if they had had the
privacy of his bungalow. Whatever Harry said, it was Ben's
sense of guilt about loving his brother's wife, a guilt Abby
had stirred with her hit-home truths, that had brought him
to the point of striking her—not that he had any sense of
responsibility towards Abby herself.

Ben rattled the key in her lock and silently pushed the
door open for her to enter. The sheer luxury of the room
overwhelmed her for a few moments as she took in the
large-sized bed which still left plenty of room for heavily
carved Spanish-style long dressers and chest of drawers as
well as a writing desk situated near double glass sliding
doors leading to the balcony. The only part not covered
by the thick mushroom-coloured carpet was a meticulously
clean bathroom to her left. Ben put her suitcase on the
stand provided for it and she asked:

'Where's your room?' her eyes sparkling at the thought
of spending even a few days in such luxury.

He glanced at the other key in his hand. 'Right next door
—so if you're lonely in the night you'll only have to knock
on the wall and I'll be here.'

The sparkle faded from her eyes and she turned away to
walk a few paces into the bedroom. 'Pity it's not your
brother and his wife's room, isn't it? Then you would only
have to wait till he's asleep bef——'

Her breath was whipped from her body when he came up
behind her and jerked her round to meet his blazing eyes.
'What does it take to convince you?' he gritted. 'Another
dose of the same? I warn you, Abby, it's you who'll feel a
fool if you carry on like this in front of my family.'

Fear shivered down her spine at the murderous look in
his eyes, but she managed to pull herself from his grip and
say with her back to him: 'Don't worry, Ben, I won't give
your guilty secret away!'

She blinked at the heartfelt oaths he uttered behind her,
but he made no attempt to touch her again. After a few
moments when he seemed to be collecting himself suffici-

ently to be able to speak normally, he said tightly: 'I'll pick you up in half an hour—that should give you time to change into something more feminine, if you possess such a thing!'

Only the click of the door told her he had gone, and she let out a long sigh as she went slowly to the windows to look out uncaring at the dried grass hills in the distance. Was it possible that Ben's words had been a genuine warning, that he didn't care for Sylvia in that way? But if that was so, why had they greeted each other so enthusiastically? Why the whispered words at their parting if it wasn't to arrange a later meeting when their reunion would have the cloak of privacy?

The faint sound of water running in the bathroom next door reminded her that Ben would be coming shortly to call for her, and she went to get ready herself for the meeting with his family.

Abby immediately forgot any qualms she had had about meeting Ben's father the instant the older man rose from his chair near the windows of his sitting room. White hair did little to camouflage the likeness his son bore him in every respect but in his eyes, which were a deep dark blue.

Ben would look like this when he grew older, she thought involuntarily as the older man enfolded her hand in his politely before turning to unashamedly embrace the son he had not seen for so long. Moments of silent communion passed between the two, and Abby felt tears prickle the back of her eyes so that she wasn't surprised to see a suspicion of moisture in Ben's when he at last drew away from his father after a final pat from the gnarled hand.

'How are you, Dad?' he asked, his voice emotionally husky.

'All the better for seeing you, son! If I'd known old Eddie was going to keep you that long in Texas I'd never have let you go—and then——'

'He needed me, Dad,' Ben interrupted quietly. 'There was nobody else he could rely on to do things his way.'

His father chuckled. 'No, that sounds like Ed all right.' To Abby, he twinkled: 'This old friend of mine in Texas—why, even his own son couldn't do things to his liking, so he upped and left the ranch, but this boy of mine managed the ranch and Eddie too!'

Abby smiled, and looked curiously at Ben. Masterful, yes, and capable enough to run a ranch ten times the size of Cedar Hills—but handling a man ornery enough to have set his own son against ranching? Her thoughts were interrupted at that point by the arrival of Sylvia and her husband, Ben's brother George. The meeting between the brothers was almost as emotional as that between father and son, and Abby felt a stab of what might have been jealousy at the genuine closeness this family enjoyed compared to her own meagre background in human relationships. Harry had done her best, but she hadn't been flesh and blood as these people were to each other. Her own father had had the warmth taken from him when his wife died and left him with a girl he didn't know how to show his love for.

It didn't seem surprising when George, like Ben in the leanness of face and frame but darker of hair and eyes, took her in his arms and kissed her cheek in welcome.

'You're even prettier than Ben wrote,' he smiled, his eyes going appreciatively from her red-gold hair to faintly flushed cheeks and calf-length dress of frothy midnight blue chiffon. Ben's eyes had registered shock when he had collected her in her room and, although he hadn't said anything, she sensed that he was pleased with her appearance to meet the rest of his family.

'Ben?' George said without releasing her waist as he looked over his shoulder at his brother. 'These girls look so pretty, I think we should take them dancing. How about it?'

Ben smiled, a slow smile in eyes that took in Abby's tautly held slenderness in his brother's arms then ran lightly over Sylvia's dress in tawny shades of silk. 'Fine,' he agreed easily, turning to his father, who had seated himself again. 'There's a dinner dance right here in the hotel, Dad—will you come down with us?'

'From the way you asked that,' the white-haired patriarch told him, 'it seems as if that's the only way I'm going to see my family for the rest of the day. I'll come down for a while, then leave you young people to enjoy yourselves without an old man getting in your way.'

'Oh, but you wouldn't be doing that!' Abby surprised even herself when the words came out and she moved from George's loose grasp to go to the older man. It was illogical, ridiculous, that she should feel this fierce protectiveness so soon after meeting Ben's father, but feel it she did, and her sincerity was real when she knelt beside his chair and put a hand on his beige-suited sleeve. 'Please come, Mr Franklin, and stay a while after dinner. It's a family reunion for Ben, and it wouldn't be the same without you.'

His hand, knotted through time and work, covered hers and patted it, but he seemed to wince and look accusingly at Ben before answering: 'Thank you, honey, it's nice of you to say that, but I was young myself once and I know you young people like to be on your own without an old man's eyes on you all the time. We'll all eat together, then I'll leave you to it. My old bones don't take kindly to tripping the light fantastic any more.' His eyes twinkled kindly into Abby's as she knelt beside him. 'You know, you remind me of—' he made a dismissing gesture when Ben took a step towards them '—of my wife when she was your age. She was a beautiful girl too, but oh, my—temper!' His head shook despairingly. 'I thought I never would get her to the altar, she bucked every inch of the way.'

'But she did go,' Abby reminded him with a smile.

'Oh, yes, she went,' he chuckled reminiscently, 'after I'd turned her over my knee a couple of times and beat some sense into her!' He seemed not to notice the swift startled look Abby threw Ben, who stood nearby frowning thoughtfully, the wary look she knew so well visible in his eyes.

'Anyway,' his father went on unheedingly, 'after I gave her a few babies to care for, she quietened down considerably. Not that she ever lost her spirit—that wouldn't have been my Marianne at all.' From the proud way he said this, Abby gathered that the last thing he would have wanted was a meekly docile wife who did his bidding without question.

'She must have loved you very much,' she said, not knowing why she felt a sudden affinity with Ben's mother except that she suspected she herself would never lose her

free-tongued determination of spirit, whatever Harry said
to the contrary.

'I think she did, child, in fact I'm sure she did,' Ben's
father patted her hand again in an absent way, his dark blue
eyes looking backwards to a woman even his sons would not
have recognised.

Sylvia's light laughter came as a welcome interruption in
the emotion-laid atmosphere. 'Listen, everybody! George
and I have some family type news we think you'll like.'
Looking appealingly up into her husband's eyes, she asked:
'Is it all right to tell them now, darling?'

'It seems to me they'll know what the news is before you
get around to spilling it, honey,' he smiled lazily in a way
reminiscent of Ben, his arm settling comfortably round his
wife's waist to pull her possessively to his side.

'Oh! Well—Dad, how do you like the idea of being a
grandfather? And Ben, what do you think of becoming an
uncle after all this time?'

In the resulting confusion of family congratulations, Abby
was left at the outer rim of warmth washing over everyone
but herself. Her eyes were large puzzled orbs as they
watched Ben kiss Sylvia's cheek, then turn to shake his
brother's hand with a delighted smile and a remark Abby
didn't quite hear. Her ears were roaring instead with pound-
ing blood that told her how wrong she had been about Ben
—he hadn't been in love with his brother's wife, not in the
sense Abby understood. But why hadn't he made it clear
to her? Right from the start, from that night coming home
from Debby's barbecue, he had let her know that he loved
Sylvia. Was this just an act? Could anyone possibly pretend
to be as pleased at this moment as Ben was at the prospect of
becoming an uncle?

He came to her, his eyes revealing none of the smugness
of 'I told you so' that she might have expected. Instead, he
put an arm round her waist and drew her into the family
circle so that she seemed one with them, keeping his arm
firmly there while she congratulated Sylvia and George.

The dazed sense of unreality grew rather than lessened
throughout the meal they all shared in the dimly lit restau-
rant where they were a party alone in a plushly upholstered

nook in one corner. Abby scarcely tasted the prime ribs of Alberta beef, but the others seemed not to notice her abstraction, although several times Ben's enigmatic gaze was bent on her when she glanced up.

Why hadn't he made it clear that he wasn't in love with Sylvia? Had he been afraid that Abby would read more into his casual kisses than he intended, so making Sylvia his shield against an entanglement he had no desire for? Looking at him now, where he sat beside Sylvia and laughed at something she was saying, Abby knew there must have been many girls in his twenty-nine years who would have been more than happy to extend what was to him a casual affair into something more meaningful. How many times had he used Sylvia in this way?

The question niggled at her until, when Ben took her in his arms to dance after his father's departure for his suite, her voice came out as a sharp probe.

'Why didn't you tell me, Ben?' she asked coldly, and felt him stiffen.

'Tell you what?'

'That you're not in love with Sylvia—that way.'

In the subdued lighting she saw the quick white gleam of his teeth in a smile that could have denoted relief. 'Did I ever tell you I was in love with her—that way?' he murmured, bending his head so that his breath fanned warmly over her ear.

'You let me think you were!' Abby lifted her head at the same time he did and found his mouth poised only a fraction away from hers. Swallowing hard, she added weakly: 'You know you did.'

His head moved that fraction and she felt his lips, warm and seductively probing, on hers. 'I didn't tell you that,' he said huskily a moment later, his arm holding her with a strength that took the breath from her. 'You jumped to that conclusion when I told you I loved her.'

'Isn't that—the same thing?' she asked, having difficulty with her breathing against the hard outline of his chest.

'Of course not. There's more than one kind of love in the world, Abby. I believe I said to you at the time that you wouldn't understand the kind of love I have for Sylvia.'

'I thought you meant——'

She paused and he rubbed his cheek against her hair in mute reproof, saying thickly a moment later: 'No, it's not the kind of love a man has for the woman in his life. I feel for Sylvia as I'd have felt for a sister if I'd had one.'

Abby forced her head back to look enquiringly into his face. '*Is* there a woman in your life, Ben?'

Her heart almost stopped beating as he moved without speaking or even looking at her, then his eyes met and held hers so that she felt she was drowning in the meaning he beamed down at her.

'You know damn well there is,' he muttered almost angrily, 'but . . .' His feet stopped moving abruptly and he thrust her from him, though still retaining a grip on her hand. 'Let's go upstairs, Abby, I have to talk to you.'

Talk? Her mind whirled as he pulled her unceremoniously back to the table where Sylvia and George had just returned from dancing, their arms twined round each other in the dimness of the alcove seat.

'Abby's tired,' Ben announced tersely. 'I'm taking her upstairs, so we'll say goodnight.'

'Goodnight, honey,' Sylvia smiled up at Abby in a friendly way that brought an answering smile. 'We'll get together tomorrow when these men of ours are out looking the bulls over.'

It was on the tip of Abby's tongue to say that if Ben went looking for bulls for Cedar Hills, she would want to be there, but the words died before they had formed. A thrill had run through her at Sylvia's casual reference to 'these men of ours' and suddenly nothing else seemed to matter. Nothing, that is, except Ben's warm hand which seemed to burn through the flimsy material of her gown and reach the soft skin beneath it.

'Goodnight, Abby, see you tomorrow,' George unwound his long frame to say, ' 'night, Ben.'

The brothers made hasty arrangements to meet the following morning, then Ben was leading Abby from the dining room, only Abby noticing the tall dark girl dancing by with an older man, her jaw dropping in surprise when she caught sight of Ben.

At Abby's door Ben hesitated. 'Can I come in for a minute, Abby? There's something I have to say to you, and I don't want to say it here in the corridor.'

Abby's calmly worded: 'Of course, Ben,' belied the agitated hammer of her heart as she went ahead into the room, a flick of the light switch bringing a rosily subdued aura to the silhouetted blue of her dress as she turned close to the bed and faced Ben. What else could he want to say but that he had wanted her to find out for herself how unimportant Sylvia was to him as a woman, that he loved Abby in the same way as she loved him?

'There's something I have to tell you, Abby,' he began hoarsely. 'Something I should have told you a long time ago, but——' He broke off, his hands sliding up the bareness of her arms to clasp tightly near her shoulders. 'You liked my family well enough, didn't you, Abby?'

'More than any people I've ever known, apart from Harry,' she replied honestly. 'I wish I'd had the kind of family life you've known, Ben. One where everybody cares so much about everybody else, but—' she sighed deeply '—Dad tried, but it wasn't the same for him when my mother died.'

'No ... it's been the same with my father.' His voice sounded strained, and all at once Abby wanted to hold him, be held by him, know the kind of love shared by his brother and Sylvia. 'Abby, I have to tell you——'

She put a finger across his lips and looked up at him contritely. 'There's something I have to tell you first, Ben. I'm sorry—so very sorry—that I thought you and Sylvia ... well, that I thought you were having an affair.' Her voice lowered a notch. 'You were quite right to—to spank me that time when I——'

'Oh, Abby!'

Ben shook his head from side to side despairingly, then his eyes fastened on the moist parting of her lips and with a groan he bent his head swiftly to take possession of them with a fierce hunger that rocked and frightened her at first, then sent a languorous, creeping flame of desire through her body until she was clinging to him mindlessly. Opening her lips to the crushing force of his, she neither knew nor cared when he lifted her to the bed and lay there with her, the pulsing hardness of his body stirring the wordless desires buried deep within her. Consciousness faded until there was only Ben at the centre of her universe, the pinnacle of the fantasy mountain she had erected in her imagination an easily climbed surface now ...

Disappointed, breathless, she felt Ben's weight lift from her and focused her eyes dimly on his white-faced figure beside the bed. 'Ben?' she whispered entreatingly, lifting her hands and feeling them clasped in his as he pulled her to her feet. 'Ben, don't go. I—I love you, Ben.'

His arms went round her and his mouth went from her neck across her softly rounded jaw to her lips, fastening there for only a few fleeting moments before he said huskily against them:

'I have to leave—right now, or I'll never go at all.' His long fingers cupped her face, his eyes blazed agonisedly down into hers. 'I love you too, Abby, more than anyone or anything I've ever loved in my life. But——' His arms dropped away from her and he clenched his jaw as if seeking for control. 'I'll see you tomorrow, Abby,' he said with sudden bleakness that chased the warmth from her veins.

'Ben?' she called softly, but he had already gone, and she fell back on the bed, tears doing little to alleviate the tension he had built up in her. He had said he loved her, but what did that mean when he walked out on her immediately after? Leaving her with a nameless ache she didn't know how to cope with. Was Ben feeling that way, too? If only he had stayed a little longer ... if only she could see him for a few minutes ... she caught her breath when she heard his bedroom door click. Was he coming back? Breathlessly she waited for his knock, but none came and she knew he must have returned to the lower floor, too restless, like herself, to go to bed and sleep easily.

Sliding her feet into the sandals that had slipped from her feet and obliterating the tears from her face, she snatched up her purse and thrust her room key into it. There must be somewhere quiet in the hotel where they could talk, somewhere not as intimate as a bedroom ... Ben had said he had something to tell her, and he had left before doing so.

His dark-suited figure had gone from the elevator hall, and Abby summoned another one by pressing hard on the 'Down' button, hoping she would catch him before he returned to the dining room where George and Sylvia probably still were. To her relief, she saw his wide shoulders crossing the hall just ahead of her when she reached the lobby, his destination obviously the bar situated just beyond the dining room. She was just about to call out to him when a girl, the dark girl who had seemed to recognise him when they were leaving the dining room, came from there alone and bumped into him. Making no attempt to disguise her delight, the girl gave him a wide smile.

'*Ben*! Ben West! I thought I recognised you earlier, but I couldn't be sure. It's so dark in the dining room and it's been such ages since you've been around home. What are you doing with yourself?'

Ben—*West*? Abby's lips parted in a gasp of disbelief. The girl must have made a mistake, but how strange that she should have chosen the name of West, the one Abby hated above all others! And then suddenly she knew there was no mistake, because Ben, angling himself slightly to the other side of the girl, was chatting to her as if it was quite normal for her to address him with that name.

His words were indistinguishable, but Abby's eyes, wide and darkened to navy with shock, seemed mesmerised on his lean, clear-cut profile. Her feet were glued to the floor, her limbs paralysed until Ben, seeming to sense her presence, looked round and saw her. For long moments their eyes locked and held, communicating without words Abby's horror at his deception and Ben's silent plea for her understanding. The dark girl, seeing his abstraction, looked over at Abby too, a frown marring her brow when she recognised the girl Ben had been escorting from the dining room earlier.

'Abby.' Ben's lips formed her name soundlessly, and the movement seemed to unlock Abby's clenched muscles and give her the strength to whirl round and run back towards the elevators, Ben's peremptory 'Abby!' speeding rather than impeding the force of her retreat. He pushed into the elevator beside her as the doors were closing, his face a sickly white beneath the deep tan as he grasped her shoulders.

'Listen to me, Abby,' he said urgently. 'That's what I was going to tell you tonight, but——'

'Take your hands off me, Ben *West*!' she spat at him, wrenching her shoulders away from his grip and rushing into the corridor as soon as the doors opened on the sixth floor. Ben caught up with her outside her door as she fumbled in her purse for the key.

'Abby, you have to listen to me!' Taking the key from her hand, he inserted it in the lock and threw the door open.

'I don't entertain *Wests* in my bedroom!' she said bitingly, remaining on the threshold.

His voice had taken on a note of grim determination when he reached for her hand and jerked her into the room, banging the door behind them. 'This is one West you're going to *listen* to in your bedroom. Sit down!'

'I'll call the desk and tell them you're bothering me,' she snapped, crossing to the telephone on the bedside table.

'I said *sit down*!' he barked, and she subsided suddenly on the edge of the bed, though her eyes still sparkled dangerously when she looked defiantly up at him.

'I should have known you were a West,' she scorned. 'Brute force is the only way they know how to handle women.'

'You know nothing about the Wests,' he told her savagely, coming to stand over her like an avenging devil. 'You made up your mind that we're all male chauvenists out to beat you down at every opportunity because you're female. It didn't enter your mind that my father—all of us!— might want to help a girl left alone to run a sizeable ranch, especially when your father had explicitly asked him to do just that. And to see that you didn't marry any self-seeking Dave Corbens!'

Abby's head jerked up, her eyes puzzled and disbelieving. 'Oh, yes,' Ben nodded, 'your father knew everything wasn't on the up-and-up with Corben, but he wasn't able to prove anything because of his state of health. Whatever Corben said, the last thing your father wanted was for you to marry him. I could see why from the first time I saw you, when he was putting on the he-man act he could only keep up in front of a girl.'

Silence reigned while Abby digested this, then she looked up and said: 'You've been a liar right from the beginning, when you said your name was Ben Franklin. Why?' She was unaware of her childishly disappointed appeal.

His lips twisted in a sardonic smile. 'Would you have welcomed me with open arms if I'd said I was Ben West? I hadn't meant to deceive you that way, but when I arrived everybody, including you, seemed to take it for granted that I was the new man you were expecting. I found out later when I spoke to the Labour man in town that the real new man took the job further north, so I didn't do him out of a job. Anyway, I wasn't lying. My name is Ben Franklin—I told you my mother was a very proud American.'

'But—but the Wests only had two sons,' she accused, bewildered.

'They did—when my father moved to Alberta. John and Linc were born there, and I guess your father never heard about them.'

'And the rest?' she asked quietly, her lashes lowered to make golden halos on her cheeks. 'The—the kisses ... the lovemaking—was all that just to fulfill my father's wishes and see that I didn't marry Dave Corben?'

'No!' Ben dropped to the bed beside her and lifted her tightly clasped hands from her lap, covering them with his. 'I knew the minute I saw you there in the office with Corben that you were the one I'd waited for, the one I'd want to spend the rest of my life with. The problem was in convincing you of that—especially when you found out that I was a West ...' His fingers tilted her chin up. 'Every time you talked about the Wests and how you hated us made it more difficult for me to tell you who I was.'

'That policeman—Sergeant Mathers—knew who you were, didn't he?' she asked with sudden certainty.

'Yes. I had to tell him in case he made enquiries and found out who I really was.'

'And the phone call you made to the Wests—something bothered me about it at the time, but I couldn't think what. You didn't ask for the West's number—because you already knew it!' Abby slapped her forehead. 'What a fool I was not to have known ... the way you defended the Wests all the time ... the way you took more interest in the ranch than any ordinary foreman would have ...'

Ben sat with tightly closed mouth, saying nothing as her memory took her back over his time at Cedar Hills, letting her come to her own conclusions about his actions.

Finally, she said, looking directly up into his eyes: 'And that's why you were such a bear coming down here, wasn't it? Because you were going to tell me who you were, not that—you were strung up about seeing Sylvia again.'

'Was I a bear?' he said softly, one finger rubbing tentatively against her cheek. 'I guess it was because I knew I couldn't ask you to marry me until you knew who I was, and I didn't know how you would take it. I hoped that when you met some of my family you'd look on me with a kinder eye.' He frowned. 'You did like them, didn't you, before you knew they were Wests? Dad took to you right off, I could tell. You remind him of Mom, and he loved her the way I love you. She was a handful,' he smiled wryly, his other hand coming up to run through the red-gold of Abby's hair, 'but he managed her just the way I mean to manage you.'

Abby straightened away from the hypnotic effect his fingers were having, her eyes snapping with instant mutiny. 'No man manages *me*!' she declared, 'least of all a——'

'Abby!' he warned, then silenced her by covering her lips with his own and forcing her back until her head touched the pillow. Abby felt the anger drain from her as his searching mouth substituted other feelings of a much more urgent nature, his hands reinforcing the ardent message of his lips as they caressed her body with increasing demand until she pulled her head away and gasped:

'I think we should get married, Ben.'

His lazy smile roved over her face an inch away from his. 'Are you asking me or telling me?'

'Neither,' she responded quickly, her eyes intent on the

tantalising nearness of his well-shaped mouth. 'That's up to you.'

'Good—you're improving,' he murmured, kissing lightly over her skin but smiling with his voice. 'In that case, will you marry me, Abigail Mackenzie?'

'Yes, please,' she whispered in a voice that conveyed fully the drowning sensation she was feeling.

'There's only one problem,' Ben lifted his head to say.

'Problem? What problem?'

'Do you sweep me off to your castle, or do I sweep you off to mine?'

Abby's eyes sprang open and gazed into his. 'Do you have a castle?'

'Not as such,' he admitted, 'but we all have equal shares in the family property. We could build a house there and——'

'But there's already a house waiting for us at Cedar Hills,' she protested, then smiled as she wound her arms round his neck. 'Nearly half of it belongs to the Wests anyway—how much equality can you have?'

'You and your equality,' he growled, and had barely reclaimed her lips when she pulled away, frowning.

'What's wrong now?' he asked resignedly.

'Children.'

'Children?'

'Ours. They'd be bound to have red hair.' She sounded so distressed that he stroked gently through the offending gold of hers.

'Does that matter?' he asked huskily, his eyes bemused as they went over her face and settled on the inviting fullness of her mouth. 'As long as they don't inherit their mother's temper to go with it . . .'

'Ben Franklin!—West,' she added belatedly. 'You haven't the sweetest temper in the world yourself!'

'Me?' He lifted his head, amazed. 'I'm the most even-tempered man you'll ever find—ask anybody who knows me.'

'I know you, and I've been on the receiving end of your temper,' she reminded him.

'Oh, that,' he dismissed, pulling himself further on to

the bed so that his body followed closely the contours of hers. 'That was a cool, calm decision to bring you back into line when you were getting beyond reason. I might be driven to do it again,' he warned, then relaxed the full weight of his hard form on hers and nuzzled her ear. 'But these surroundings seem a lot better for resolving our differences!'

'Yes, Ben,' she murmured docilely, not even hearing the feminine surrender in her agreement.

Harlequin

COLLECTION
EDITIONS OF 1978

50 great stories of special beauty and significance

$1.25
each novel

In 1976 we introduced the first 100 Harlequin Collections—a selection of titles chosen from our best sellers of the past 20 years. This series, a trip down memory lane, proved how great romantic fiction can be timeless and appealing from generation to generation. The theme of love and romance is eternal, and, when placed in the hands of talented, creative, authors whose true gift lies in their ability to write from the heart, the stories reach a special level of brilliance that the passage of time cannot dim. Like a treasured heirloom, an antique of superb craftsmanship, a beautiful gift from someone loved—these stories too, have a special significance that transcends the ordinary. **$1.25 each novel**

Here are your 1978
Harlequin Collection Editions...

Original Harlequin Romance numbers in brackets

ORDER FORM
Harlequin Reader Service

In U.S.A.
MPO Box 707
Niagara Falls, N.Y. 14302

In Canada
649 Ontario St.,
Stratford, Ontario, N5A 6W2

Please send me the following Harlequin Collection novels. I am enclosing my check or money order for $1.25 for each novel ordered, plus 25¢ to cover postage and handling.

☐ 102	☐ 115	☐ 128	☐ 140
☐ 103	☐ 116	☐ 129	☐ 141
☐ 104	☐ 117	☐ 130	☐ 142
☐ 105	☐ 118	☐ 131	☐ 143
☐ 106	☐ 119	☐ 132	☐ 144
☐ 107	☐ 120	☐ 133	☐ 145
☐ 108	☐ 121	☐ 134	☐ 146
☐ 109	☐ 122	☐ 135	☐ 147
☐ 110	☐ 123	☐ 136	☐ 148
☐ 111	☐ 124	☐ 137	☐ 149
☐ 112	☐ 125	☐ 138	☐ 150
☐ 113	☐ 126	☐ 139	☐ 151
☐ 114	☐ 127		

Number of novels checked @
$1.25 each = $ _____
N.Y. and N.J. residents add
appropriate sales tax $ _____

Postage and handling $ ___.25___

                         TOTAL $ _____

NAME _____
                    (Please Print)
ADDRESS _____

CITY _____

STATE/PROV. _____

ZIP/POSTAL CODE _____

ROM 2223

A

Offer expires December 31, 1978

And there's still *more* love in

Do you have a favorite
Harlequin author?
Then here is an
opportunity you must
not miss!